MUSIC FOR CHILDREN

**Orff-Schulwerk
American Edition**

**Volume 3
Upper Elementary**

**based on
Carl Orff — Gunild Keetman
MUSIK FÜR KINDER**

contributions by

Tossi Aaron • Cynthia Campbell • Isabel Carley • Nancy Ferguson • Jane Frazee • Ruth Pollock Hamm • Lynn W. Johnson • Maureen Kennedy • Marcia Lunz • Erik Nielsen • Sue Ellen Page • Becky Pinnell • Martha Pline • Konnie Saliba • Miriam Samuelson • Donald Slagel • Patsy Smith • Arvida Steen • Judith Thomas

articles by

Tossi Aaron • Patricia Brown • Isabel Carley • Jane Frazee • Miriam Samuelson • Mary Stringham-Shamrock

co-ordination

Hermann Regner (Orff-Institute Salzburg)

MUSIC FOR CHILDREN Volume 3
ORFF-SCHULWERK   American Edition

Copyright © 1980 by Schott Music Corp.

ISBN 0-930448-04-9

CONTENTS

Introduction
    Explanation of Terminology v
    Keys and Compasses of Instruments vi
    Explanatory Notes vii
    Identification Symbols viii
    Photography ix

Part 1 1
Part 2 97
Part 3 199

Articles
    Patricia Brown/The Orff Instrumentarium:
        What is its Purpose? 320
    Isabel Carley/About Improvisation 322
    Tossi Aaron/Performing: Pro and Con 327
    Jane Frazee/Listening: A Participatory Approach 328
    Mary Stringham-Shamrock/Orff-Schulwerk
        and World Musics — Some Considerations 332
    Miriam Samuelson/About Dance Notation 333

Acknowledgements 335
Index 336
Alphabetical Index 341

Introduction

Volume III of the American Edition of Orff-Schulwerk is presented two years after the publication of Volume II. This volume is intended for children in the upper elementary levels and all contributions in the book have been the result of working directly with children of this age group.

The assumption should not be made that all children must experience the music and movement material of Volume II before Volume III. Because Orff-Schulwerk is often begun rather late with children, it is not possible to consider all the problems in all the learning areas systematically. For this reason we have included some songs, speech pieces and instrumental exercises in Part 1 of this volume which are suitable for newcomers to Orff-Schulwerk. One may omit parts of this section with children who have had more experiences with the more difficult exercises of Volume II.

In choosing and compiling the contributions of 20 authors we had to make a decision concerning which was most important: variety of material, or a systematic presentation of the material. We decided to compromise and form small units dealing either with subject area or degree of difficulty. Consequently, there is a kind of spiral of learning in movement and music which recur from time to time in increasing levels of difficulty.

We feel that music education is dependent upon the emotional involvement of both teacher and student; that language, music and dance are artistic media which appeal to the whole person intellectually and emotionally. We have deliberately tried to avoid being "school-teacherish" in presenting this material hoping that it will be inspiring and challenging, yet flexible. It is the task of the teacher to select material keeping in mind the maturity of the children, their readiness and technical abilities. The teacher must neither overestimate nor underestimate these factors.

The index beginning on page 320 is detailed and pedagogically oriented in order to assist the teacher with lesson planning. We have included the contributions of many authors to represent the size and diversity of the United States with its cultural variety. It has been the task of the editor to co-ordinate these materials into one volume with an emphasis on consistency and the preservation of the originality of the different contributions. Some basic decisions were made for purposes of unifying such things as the notation of Bass Xylophone parts in the treble clef. In other instances this attempt at unification was deliberately avoided when it was, for example, a question of the distribution of parts in a score, or the use of sharps and flats in the church modes for which there really are no definite rules. With this in mind, it is hoped that children will be prepared for such inconsistencies in the variegated scope of music literature.

The division of this volume into three parts roughly catalogues the texts and musical phenomena in a sequence according to 1) psychological development of the children, 2) increasing technical difficulties, and 3) areas of learning. Part 1 is concerned with pentatonic melodies, bordun accompaniments, rhythm and speech exercises. Part 2 concentrates on the introduction of cadential harmonies. Part 3 deals with tonal areas that are less familiar, such as those which occur in early and modern music as well as in music from foreign countries. It also presents more difficult tasks in improvisation and composition. The articles written for this volume include topics of interest that are of daily concern.

This volume is presented as an integral part of the complete series *Music for Children/Orff-Schulwerk American Edition.*

Hermann Regner

An Explanation of Some Terminology in this Edition Including Abbreviations

Barred Instruments

Soprano Glockenspiel	SG
Alto Glockenspiel	AG
Soprano Xylophone	SX
Alto Xylophone	AX
Bass Xylophone	BX
Soprano Metallophone	SM
Alto Metallophone	AM
Bass Metallophone	BM

Recorders

Sopranino Recorder	Si.R
Soprano Recorder	Sopr. R
Alto Recorder	Alto R
Tenor Recorder	Ten. R
Bass Recorder	Bass R

Timpani, Drums and Other Percussion Instruments

Bass Drum	BD
Bongo Drums	Bongo
Claves	Cl
Conga Drums	Conga
Cow Bell	CB
Cymbals	C
Finger Cymbals	FC
Guiro or Reco-Reco	G
Hand Drum	HD
Hanging Cymbals	HC
Maracas or Rattles	Mar
Sleigh Bells or Bells	SB
Snare Drum	SD
Tambourine	Tamb
Temple Block	TB
Timpani	Timp
Triangle	Tr
Wood Block	WB

Strings

Bass Viol or Violoncello	Bass
Violoncello	Vc

Mallets

With Wooden or Hard Rubber Heads	
With Felt or Other Soft Heads	

Keys and compasses of instruments

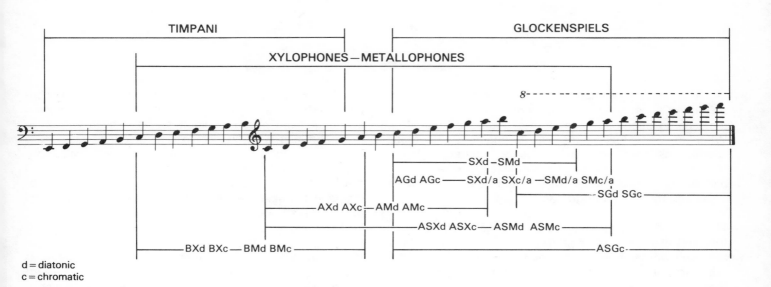

d = diatonic
c = chromatic

Sound Gestures

The separate or combined actions of finger snapping, hand clapping, thigh slapping, foot stamping.

Patsch

A German word for which there is no succinct English equivalent, describing the sound gesture of thigh slapping. In this edition the word has been anglicized to include the forms: patching, patched, etc. Patsching is slapping the thighs with one or both hands in a relaxed and bouncing way. It is used in rhythmic exercises and for the preparation of instrumental playing.

Non-pitched instruments

Small percussion instruments that have no definite pitch (claves, wood block, tambourine, hand drum, rattle, sleigh bells, cymbals, etc.)

Explanatory Notes

■ This edition is intended as a teachers' guide. Not only does it contain a rich collection of material but also many suggestions for use in the course of teaching. When the individual teacher is in agreement with these suggestions, then they may be used as they stand. If the teacher feels that because of personality or for reasons of particular classroom situations it would be better to make a change, then it is right to do so.

■ The pedagogical suggestions are not recipes to be followed ingredient for ingredient, but on the one hand are intended to ease the task of the teacher and on the other are merely comments from the contributors about their own experiences. All pieces have been proven in classes with children. It may happen that many of the examples can be worked out with children rather quickly in a short period of time; others may need longer periods of preparation for development.

■ Some of the songs in this edition, especially those of folk origin, are known in other melodic forms. Choose the melody you are familiar with, or the one the children know in their particular area.

■ It is possible to combine different pieces for purposes of creating a larger music and/or movement form. A song, for example, followed by an instrumental piece in similar or contrasting character can extend the form.

■ It was especially difficult to make a decision concerning the notation for bass instruments. Parts for bass xylophone and bass metallophone have been written in the treble clef with an octave sign below to facilitate a change to another instrument if necessary. In addition, the use of the treble clef makes it easier to comprehend the full score at a glance. The notation for timpani remains in the bass clef. It is also possible to use plucked or bowed stringed instruments as bass parts, (guitar, lute, gamba, cello).

■ There are some instruments whose tonal quality is such that it is extremely difficult to blend with the Orff instrumentarium, e.g. melodicas or electronic instruments; therefore it is recommended that they are not used in this way.

Identification Symbols

Sample Lesson

Listening Activity

Speech Piece

Notation Skills

Photographs

We thank the following individuals and institutions for their contributions.

Contributor	Page
Clara Fidler, John Strange School—Indianapolis, Indiana	iii
Marilynne Blanc, Arts Magnet School—Oakland, California	iv
Marilynne Blanc, Arts Magnet School—Oakland, California	v
Manfred Perchermeier, American School—Berchtesgarten, W. Germany	vi
Marilynne Blanc, Arts Magnet School—Oakland, California	vii
Marilynne Blanc, Arts Magnet School—Oakland, California	1
Marilynne Blanc, Arts Magnet School—Oakland, California	7
Marilynne Blanc, Arts Magnet School—Oakland, California	18
Clara Fidler, John Strange School—Indianapolis, Indiana	24
Manfred Perchermeier, American School—Berchtesgarten, W. Germany	32
Marilynne Blanc, Arts Magnet School—Oakland, California	63
Marilynne Blanc, Arts Magnet School—Oakland, California	178
Marilynne Blanc, Arts Magnet School—Oakland, California	203
Marilynne Blanc, Arts Magnet School—Oakland, California	206
Marilynne Blanc, Arts Magnet School—Oakland, California	249
Marilynne Blanc, Arts Magnet School—Oakland, California	285
Marilynne Blanc, Arts Magnet School—Oakland, California	293
Marilynne Blanc, Arts Magnet School—Oakland, California	299
Manfred Perchermeier, American School—Berchtesgarten, W. Germany	303
Ruth Hamm. (Earl J. Stutzman, Photographer)—Anton Crdina School—Cleveland	318
Manfred Perchermeier, American School—Berchtesgarten, W. Germany	320
Manfred Perchermeier, American School—Berchtesgarten, W. Germany	323
Marilynne Blanc, Arts Magnet School—Oakland, California	324

PART
1

Singing is the most important activity. Pentatonic melodies are a continuation of previous experiences and are also intended for those children to whom the experience is new. Major, minor and modal melodies complete the repertoire of songs in Part 1. Songs with foreign language texts should be sung in the original language. Canons lead directly to part singing. While the technical aspects of singing are also important at this age, voice training, breathing and speech exercises should be used in small doses, so that children retain the spontaneity of singing for fun.

Instrumental playing does not require previous experience. Consideration has also been made for those children unfamiliar with the Orff Instrumentarium. Experienced teachers should find ways to include other instruments in addition to the ones presented here, especially strings and winds (See Article: Page 320: "The Orff Instrumentarium: What is its Purpose?"). It is important to rotate players frequently to give all children the opportunity to participate.

Reading and writing in this volume are not presented in a systematic sequence. It is recommended that the teacher use rhythmic and melodic excerpts from the pieces as reading and writing exercises. Singing and playing should not be laden with too much theory. When the children, however, want to remember their spontaneous music for the purpose of repeating it another time, notation is indispensable. Reading and writing music must also be practiced. A valuable audo-visual aid for this is the Orff-Instrumentarium.

Movement is very often combined with songs or instrumental pieces even if it is not specifically mentioned to do so. Movement can be preparation for or accompaniment to singing and instrumental playing; or music can be the impetus for movement, dance, mime and drama. An historical dance and a folk dance from Yugoslavia could be the start for acquiring a repertoire in dance.

Rhythmic and metric exercises start with simple note values and the meter signatures of $\frac{2}{4}$, $\frac{3}{4}$, $\frac{4}{4}$, and $\frac{6}{8}$. There are more syncopated rhythms than in Volume II and a few pieces with changing meter. It is important to do rhythmic and metric exercises with all children. All kinds of percussion instruments — including those made by the children themselves — should be used. Very often such exercises with sound gestures and instruments can be combined with reading and writing activities. Making up exercises using different rhythms, by means of improvising, repeating, improving and finally writing down, is the first step toward composition. There is no problem with having to consider harmonic structure.

1. Old Ark

The sign **|** means a cluster of pentatonic notes.

Remove the B and E bars from the instrument; strike the instrument with a bar held horizontally in the hand.
Change pitches on each beat.

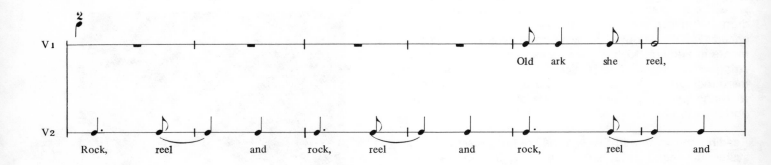

V₁: Old ark she reel,

V₂: Rock, reel and rock, reel and rock, reel and

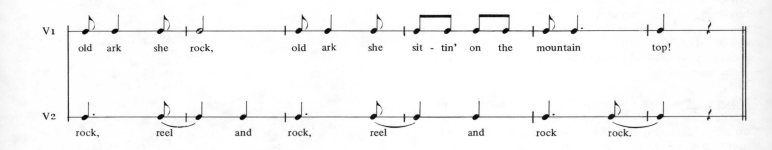

V₁: old ark she rock, old ark she sit-tin' on the mountain top!

V₂: rock, reel and rock, reel and rock rock.

2. Ungaresca

Tanzbuch Pierre Phalèse 16th Century,
textnote: Pandur =Policeman
andanduri =Play on words

4

6

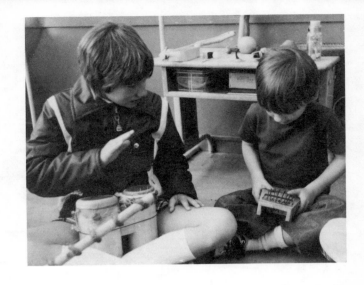

3. Patsching Exercises

These exercises for left and right hand alternation and coordination are direct preparation for instrumental playing. The patterns should be introduced initially by echoing. Patsching should always be done in a relaxed and bouncing way with dynamics. Occasionally such exercises can be used in connection with reading and writing activities. The rhythms can be transferred to instruments in pairs which produce two tones or to instru- ments which are played with two sticks (timpani, bongos, wood block, barred percussion). Notes with the stems upward are for the right hand, stems downward for the left.

- combine two, three, or four patterns
- transfer some of the patterns to barred percussion
- improvise singing or playing recorder or glockenspiel over the ostinato

from Orff–Schulwerk "Musik für Kinder" Vol. 1, p. 94

Example number 8: transferred to xylophone

4. Savila Se Bela Loza*

Each time the dance is repeated there is a slight accelerando. The last time, there is a ritardando in the last measure.

* A pretty grapevine entwined itself . . . .

Form: Circle or winding line led through room. Hands held in a relaxed, low position.

A Beginning to R with R foot, 18 light running steps and step-hop R to change direction and foot. Repeat to L starting with L foot and ending with step-hop L.

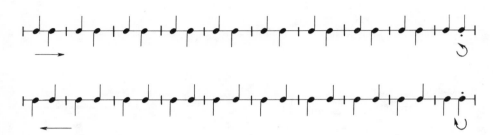

B 6 "schottisch" steps alternating between R and L: step to R with R, step with L foot slightly behind R foot, step-hop R; the same pattern to L starting with L foot.

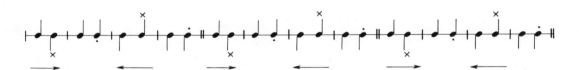

5. Smile in Your Pocket

day _____ You will ne - ver be lone - ly as you tra - vel on your way.

6. Sourwood Mountain

Kentucky Mountain Song

Chick - en crow - in' on Sour - wood Moun - tain, Hey de ding dang dil - ly dal - ly day.

So ma - ny pret - ty girls I can't count 'em! Hey de ding dang dil - ly dal - ly day.

12

Verse 2: My true love's a blue-eyed daisy, Hey de ding dang dilly dally day.
If I don't get her, I'll go crazy. Hey de ding dang dilly dally day.
Big dog bark, the little dog bite you, Hey de ding dang dilly dally day.
Big girl court you, the little one slight you. Hey de ding dang dilly dally day.

13

Movement suggestions for "Sourwood Mountain"

Stand facing a partner, right hand to right hand with palms together, right shoulder in front of partner's right shoulder. When singing the words of phrases 1, 3, 5, and 7 with quarter note pulse, point left foot out to the side, in, then right foot to the side, and in. On "Hey de ding dang dilly dally day", move forward past your partner

once again facing your partner.

Another possibility: to provide the basis of an experience in changing meters.

Keeping the same pulse, create a movement and sing the words in $\frac{3}{4}$ meter. Return to $\frac{2}{4}$ meter and the steps taught for the refrain, "Hey de ding dang".

Later repeat the song but try singing the words and making a movement pattern which is in $\frac{4}{4}$ meter, then later, in $\frac{6}{8}$. Always return to the same movement and meter of the refrain.

The challenge is to perform the song, assigning a different meter for each of the phrases 1, 3, 5, and 7, returning to the original meter and movement for each refrain.

7. An Experience With A Piece
From "Musik für Kinder"

Children in the upper grades are most fascinated with playing tunes on the barred instruments; therefore, teaching the melody first will gain their interest and challenge them musically. The students may already have learned this heritage rhyme:

> Queen, Queen, Caroline.
> Washed her hair in turpentine.*
> Turpentine made it shine,
> Queen, Queen, Caroline.

Explain that you will be singing some of the same crazy words, to help them learn the tune they will be playing.

The melody, as written, is too high to be sung comfortably, although singing is the best way to learn it. Therefore, here are several solutions: first, transpose this piece to F or G pentatonic. If you decide on the latter key, then the tune can be played by beginning recorder students (very desirable if you are short of barred instruments). Whatever key you use for the melody should be kept throughout the teaching process, since the goal is to have the children change gradually from singing to playing the melody.

The second solution is to sing the melody an octave lower than written. Although the G is low, it can be sung softly by children of 10 or 11. This solution will be used here.

If you as a teacher think the following words are a desecration of a good piece, then make up your own! Just make sure that your words reflect the phrase structure of the piece. Words, especially humorous ones, make a melody easier to learn.

Sing the following tune several times, so that the children learn it by rote. Add the snaps in the last section, which will later be played on the triangle.

* Turpentine was used as a delousing agent.

16

Analyse the phrase structure with the class. Point out that the first two phrases start the same way. Play the first measure on your xylophone, (which is reversed so that it faces the same direction as the children's instruments). At the same time sing the words. Repeat, singing letter names and have the children echo. Then have the class play the first two phrases, playing the measures they know ("Queen Caroline"), and singing the rest. Teach the endings for both phrases in the same manner, and play through both phrases.

Children with little experience may have some difficulty with beats two and three of measure 9 of the instrumental version, because of the quick change of direction involved. If measures 9 through 12, (with pick-up) are considered as four "mini-phrases", you can point out that each one ends with the notes "D-E-C", although they begin differently. Learn the beginning of each mini-phrase, pointing out their similarities and differences. Play through measures 9-12, then through the whole tune.

In teaching a tune by rote, keep the children's interest and awareness high by using a combination of activities: singing words and letter names with and without playing; "silent" playing with fingertips, singing the words "right" and "left" to indicate mallet technique. Use of both hands must be encouraged from early grades.

This procedure can take anywhere from a few minutes to several twenty minute periods.

When the tune has been learned, add the first four measures of introduction, using patching with alternate hands, and snaps for the triangle. Transfer to instruments. Have the class once again sing the tune while patching the timpani part. Select a timpani player who does not rush the eighth notes.

Next, select the students who will be playing the tune on the glockenspiels. Those who don't feel comfortable with it will probably be glad to defer to those who do, since all have had a chance to work on it.

Quickly show other players their ostinati by demonstrating on your instrument, making sure that all players know all the parts. Suggested orchestration: top line — all glockenspiels; second line — metallophones with soft beaters; third line — soprano xylophones; fourth line — alto xylophones with upper and lower voices divided; bottom line (doubled) — violoncello or bass metallophone (not playing during introduction); triangle and timpani as is. The bottom line, incidentally, outlines the phrase structure as discussed when the tune was being learned. If you do not own timpani, the bass xylophone may take that part. Finally, assign the bass part if you did not do so earlier.

In practising the ostinati, the children must take care to sing the tune as they play. Alto xylophones players must also learn their ending. All accompanying players must listen so that they do not overwheim the glockenspiels.

8. Six Instrumental Pieces

from Orff - Schulwerk: Musik für Kinder
Vol. I

1.

2.

3.

4.

6.

9. Movement With Props

Prop Possibilities
Newspaper
Paperbags
Paper plates/cups
Rope
Balls

Criteria for choosing Props
Economy
Familiarity of object
Suitability for the class
The potential that the object has
   for holding the students'
   attention

The following lesson plan involves the use of newspaper as a prop.

Exploration — of the prop with a relay race. Divide the class into two or three lines sitting or standing, depending on the movement. Give one sheet of newspaper to the first person in each line. Paper is passed to the end of the line and back to the beginning as quickly as possible using isolated body parts (e.g. elbows only, elbow and knee, two feet, knees). Repeat the race three or four times always changing the body parts used. The purpose of the race is to warm up the body.

— of actions that are possible with the prop. List on the board as many single words as possible that the students can think of which denote actions that involve a newspaper (e.g. read, fold, cover, fan, wrap, etc.). Choose one word as the stimulus for movement exploration. In this example the word "read" will be used with the prop.

Give each student a sheet of newspaper. Ask them to choose an article on their sheet of paper and to keep reading it while you are giving directions.

1. Ask them to find a comfortable position for reading — have them change positions three or four times.
Ask them to find an unusual position for reading the paper — have them change positions three or four times.

2. Repeat 1 with students working in pairs — one sheet of paper for every two students.

3. Repeat 1 and then 2 with students using an imaginary piece of paper. Experiment with the use of hands taking the place of the paper and becoming the focal point. Hands are side by side at the same distance as the newspaper was held away from the body.

— of moving in space with the prop; with an imaginary prop.

Sequencing of Exploration :

create a "group statue" with four or five students assuming positions and each one reading someone else's piece of newspaper. Practice walking in and out of the formation.

Sample Movement Composition
1. Each member of the group is reading alone
2. All come together to form "group statue"
3. Walk apart and discard paper
4. Come together again using hands as the focal point in place of the paper
5. Walk apart and end by each reading newspaper alone as in the beginning

Thematic Composition:

small groups depict a dramatic situation

Suggestions:
Delivering newspapers, paper route or news stand
Reading the morning paper at the breakfast table
Poem or quotation, e.g.
        "To everything there is a season . . .
           A time to tear,
           A time to mend." Ecclesiastes
Suggestions from the students

10. Entendez-vous le Carillon?

En - ten - dez vous le ca - ril - lon? Di ri don don don don don don don don don (don)

Canon continues ad libitum. Voices drop out one by one.

Suggestion for instrumental accompaniment.

SG

AG

AM

BM

Arrange introduction and final ending.

11. How Many Miles to Bethlehem
(Canon)

Introduction

Group I

V
SR

"How ma - ny miles to Beth - le - hem?"

SG

AG

AM

BX

Bass

Tr

BD

"Four score and ten," "Can we get there by can-dle light?" "Yes and back a-gain."

Solo: *

If your heels are nim-ble and light, you will be home by can-dle-light.

D.S.

* Words and tune from another version.

Suggestions for Playing

Introduction	Tune
BD	BD and Sopr. R.
AG, BX, and Bass	AG, BX, Bass and Voice
Full instrumentation	Full instrumentation and Voice
Full instrumentation	Full instrumentation, Sopr. R., and Voice
Full instrumentation	Full instrumentation, Sopr. R., Voice, and sung in canon.

Note: The Question-Answer form of the text clarifies the musical form **Q-A¹** , **Q-A²** particularly when 2 groups sing as marked.

12. The Little Black Bull

28

2. First he paw and then he bellow,
    Hoosen Johnny, Hoosen Johnny,
  First he paw and then he bellow,
    Long time ago.
  Chorus

3. He paw the dirt in the heifers' faces,
    Hoosen Johnny, Hoosen Johnny,
  He paw the dirt in the heifers' faces,
    Long time ago.
  Chorus

4. He whet his horn on a white oak sapling,
    Hoosen Johnny, Hoosen Johnny,
  He whet his horn on a white oak sapling,
    Long time ago.
  Chorus

5. He shake his tail and he jar the river,
    Hoosen Johnny, Hoosen Johnny,
  He shake his tail and he jar the river,
    Long time ago.
  Chorus

According to Carl Sandburg, this was Abe Lincoln's favorite song.

Note: The difference between the verse and the chorus may be made still more marked by introducing improvised unpitched percussion parts in place of those notated here.

13. The Machine

Miniature   Movement — Sound Piece

Key :

/\/\/\/\ — guiro

• • — claves

▮▮▮ — woodblock

∿∿ — alto xylophone (played with wooden mallets) glissando up

⤸ — timpani played with soft mallet then immediately dampened with elbow

 — triangle roll

⟍ — soprano recorder mouthpiece; a pitch is blown, then altered by closing the hand slowly over the mouthpiece end.

(Sequence is repeated as many times as desired)

Movement — there should be one child (or "part" of the machine) for each instrumental sound. Have the players go through the sound sequence several times, until each mover has come up with a suitable movement or action to correspond to his sound partner's instrumental sound. The piece may then be performed, either at a relatively steady pace, or with tempo changes corresponding to the starting and stopping of a machine. The guiro indicates the "hum" of the machine, and as such, need not have a person moving to it. It is the most important instrument in any tempo change, since it is constantly playing. This piece is only one of many possibilities using the "machine" idea. Other ways of approaching the idea are: have each child who is part of the machine invent a movement and a corresponding sound (made with the mouth or body). Then the child or class may pick an instrument whose sound is similar to that made by the child originally. When all the machine's movements and sounds have been chosen, put them together in a sequence and perform. The children may decide on a specific product (perhaps something totally new) which the machine manufactures, and you may wish to invent a "sound-blueprint" for the instrumental sounds (a good way of introducing graphic notation).

14. Ghost Dance Song

The Pawnees lived in Kansas and Nebraska. They are thought to have come from the southwest, since their mythology and agricultural practices are very similar to those of the Pueblo Indians. Their reverence for the sun and the moon, the morning star and the evening star are reflected in this Spirit Dance. The dancers would gather at sundown and dance all through the night until the rising of the morning star.

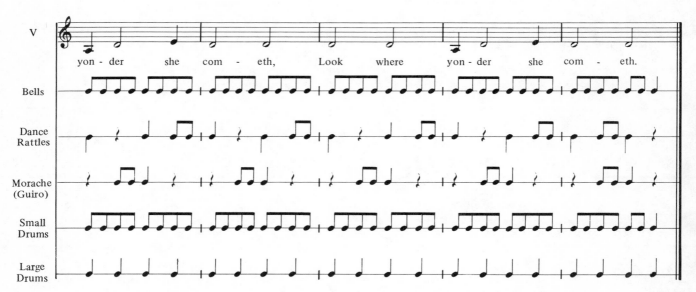

2. Stars of heaven, Stars of heaven,
   Lo, the many are coming.
   Lo, the many are coming.

3. Mother Moon, Mother Moon,
   Look where yonder she cometh,
   Look where yonder she cometh.

4. Star of Morning, Star of Morning,
   Look where yonder he cometh,
   Look where yonder he cometh.

5. Father Sun, Father Sun,
   Look where yonder he cometh,
   Look where yonder he cometh.

* Large gourd rattles, one in each hand, raised high when both are played, and at 𝆑 , shaken continuously in a descending arc until they are at waist level.

** Drums are beaten with soft padded sticks, without accents.

Reprinted from THE INDIANS BOOK by Natalie Curtis. Dover Publications, Inc. 1950.

15. Penobscot Song of Greeting

When a strange canoe was sighted, the whole village would gather at the landing to welcome the stranger. On landing, the stranger would sing the greeting song while stepping slowly towards the chief, and all the people would join in, singing "Hega, hega". When the stranger reached the chief, they would shake hands, and the stranger would say, "I greet you, Chief of the Pas-samaquoddy". Then the people would give a great shout and fire their guns. The stranger would then approach the lieutenant-chief and the leading warriors of the tribe, and greet them in the same way. Then the villagers would sing their song of greeting and welcome the visiting chief and his men in the same ceremony, before returning to the village for a feast.

Pronunciation : The consonants are like English. "E" sounds like "Ay", and "A" like "Ah". The words have no literal meaning.

* The players have a gourd or horn rattle in each hand, and alternate hands in playing. At ♯, the rattles are lifted high and shaken in a descending arc.

Reprinted from THE INDIANS BOOK by Natalie Curtis. Dover Publications, Inc., 1950.

16. Maori Indian Battle Chant

Ka - ma - tay, Ka - ma - tay, Cow - ruh, Cow - ruh. Ka - ma - tay,

Ka - ma - tay, Cow - ruh, Cow - ruh. Oo - pay - neh, Oo - pay - neh,

whee - teh, whee - teh, Oo - pay - neh, Oo - pay - neh, whee - teh, whee - teh.

- This chant can be accompanied with non-pitched percussion instruments. Try to work out a form in which instruments are added cumulatively.
- Have the children work out a dance form.

Suggestions
Verse 1: hand drums 1st beat of each measure
Verse 2: add jingle bells on each beat of each measure
Verse 3: add temple blocks on 3/2 measure ♩ ♫♩;
2/2 Measure ♪ ♪
Verse 4: add big Conga 3/3 ♩. 2/2 ♩
and whip 3/3 ♩. 2/2 ♩ — |

17. The Ball Game

A. Warm-up

1. The class loosens up by rotating the head; loosening the neck; rotating the shoulders; forwards and backwards; rotating the arms at the shoulder; rotating the torso at the waist; rotating the hips; rotating the legs at the hips; rotating the knees; rotating the feet at the ankles.

2. Each one "winds up" for the pitch, pretending to throw a baseball, using both right and left arms.

B. Pass the ball

1. The class sits in circles of 8 to 10, cross-legged, knees touching; the word "pass" is repeated in a steady beat.

2. A tennis ball is passed counter-clockwise as the teacher beats the pulse on a handrum. "Pass" is still said.

3. When the beat stops, so does the ball, but the spoken "pass" pulse is continued.

4. The class silently passes the ball with the drumbeat, stops when the beat stops, and switches the pass direction when the teacher says "switch".

5. The class repeats the words "pass-hold" as the ball is passed and held around the circle. This time, when the ⌐⌐ drumbeat stops, the class continues to pass-hold. Switching takes place and tempos can vary.

6. This is also done in triple meter, "pass-hold-hold."

7. Now the class must listen to the meter of the drum, because when it hears ⌐⌐ , the ball goes to the right, and ⌐⌐⌐ , to the left.

C. Roll the ball

1. The ball is rolled and the roller must say the name of the person to whom the ball goes.

2. The ball is now rolled in a regular pulse, "roll-catch"; as a signal, the roller looks at the person to whom it goes; it is done with and without the drumbeat.

3. The above can also be done in triple meter, "roll-catch-hold". Tempos can vary according to the drumbeat.

D. Bounce the ball

1. The circle widens, class stands, the ball is bounced clockwise to a moderate "bounce-catch" pulse.

2. The direction of the ball changes on cue from the teacher and it stops on command.

3. What happens to the ball and the space between people when the tempo is slower? faster?

4. This can also be done in triple meter, "bounce-catch-hold".

E. Throw the ball in pantomime

1. Each group now has an imaginary ball and is on its own.

2. The catcher must catch the ball as it was thrown, i.e., high, quickly with a bounce, etc.

3. It is a magic ball and may grow or shrink in weight and/or size; it can become a beach ball, golf ball, football, even a spit ball, or a ball as big as the whole group.

4. Everyone must be aware of eye contact and the size of the ball as it was given; whoever has it can change the size, etc., by pantomime.

It is possible to use the elements of this lesson in smaller units.

18. Rhythmic Exercise: Canon

A. Sound Gestures

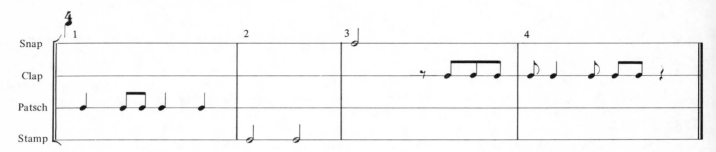

B. Non-Pitched Percussion
(separate player for each instrument)

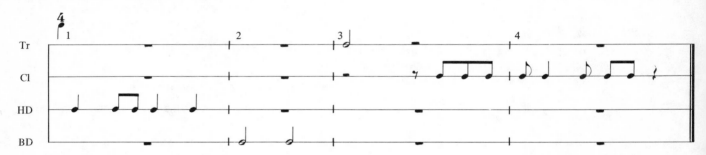

Suggestions for Preparation and Performance

1. Learn the sound gestures in unison.

2. Practice as canon in two parts, then three, finally four.

3. To prepare for B assign one sound gesture to each of four groups:

| snap | clap | patsch | stamp |

Practice in unison.

4. Sub-divide each of the above into four smaller groups:

snap	snap	snap	snap
clap	clap	clap	clap
patsch	patsch	patsch	patsch
stamp	stamp	stamp	stamp

Practice rhythm with each group.

5. Play as canon in two parts, then three, finally four. The "patscher" makes the canonic entrances for each group.

6. When all of the above is secure, transfer to non-pitched percussion and play B.

7. Add a melody above the rhythm on a recorder.

19. Drum Canon (1)

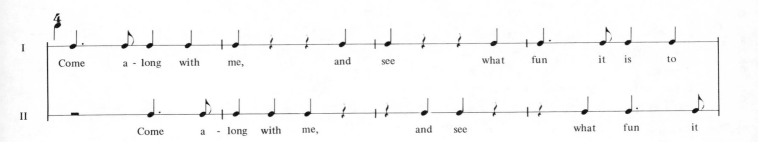

I Come a - long with me, and see what fun it is to

II Come a - long with me, and see what fun it

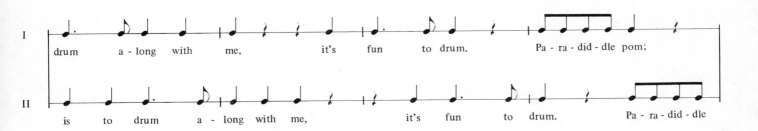

I drum a - long with me, it's fun to drum. Pa - ra - did - dle pom;

II is to drum a - long with me, it's fun to drum. Pa - ra - did - dle

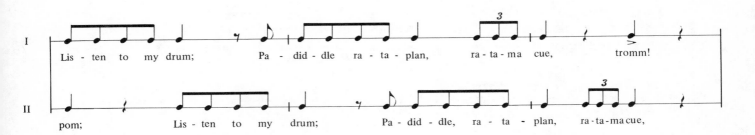

I Lis - ten to my drum; Pa - did - dle ra - ta - plan, ra - ta - ma cue, tromm!

II pom; Lis - ten to my drum; Pa - did - dle, ra - ta - plan, ra - ta - ma cue,

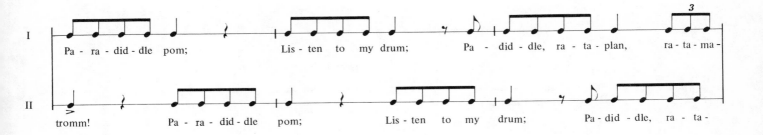

I Pa - ra - did - dle pom; Lis - ten to my drum; Pa - did - dle, ra - ta - plan, ra - ta - ma -

II tromm! Pa - ra - did - dle pom; Lis - ten to my drum; Pa - did - dle, ra - ta -

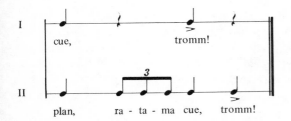

I cue, tromm!

II plan, ra - ta - ma cue, tromm!

The text helps one to memorize the rhythm to be played on the drums.

Drum Canon (2)

Version 2 is written on two lines for hand drum, using finger-thumb technique. This may also be played on other two-toned percussion instruments (i.e. bongos, tubular woodblock, congas, etc.).

* F = finger
  Th = thumb

36

20. Liebe ist ein Ring *

Traditional German Round

Lie - be ist ein Ring _____ , ein Ring hat kein

*Love is a ring: a ring has no end.

37

40

V1: ————, ein Ring hat___ kein En - - de.

V2: hat___ kein En - de.

V3: de.

Becoming gradually softer until there is no more sound.

41

21. Canon

22. Týnom, Tánom

Czechoslovakia

1. Tý - nom, tá - nom, na ko - peč - ku stá - la, Tý - nom, tá - nom, na mňa po - ze - ra - la. Tý - nom, tá - nom ne - po - ze - raj na mňa, Tý - nom, tá - nom, ne - poj - deš ty za mňa.

1. Tý-nom, tá-nom, na Kopečku stála,
   Tý-nom, tá-nom, na mňa pozerala.
   Tý-nom, tá-nom, nepozeraj na mňa,
   Tý-nom, tá-nom, nepojdeš ty za mňa.

2. Tý-nom, tá-nom, prečo by ja nešla?
   Tý-nom, tá-nom, však som ja nie pyšná.
   Tý-nom, tá-nom, královna je pyšná.
   Tý-nom, tá-nom, predsa za muž išla.

Man sings:
Tý-nom, tá-nom, she was standing on a hill
Tý-nom, tá-nom, she was looking at me.
Tý-nom, tá-nom, do not look at me,
Tý-nom, tá-nom, you shall not marry me.

Girl sings:
Tý-nom, tá-nom, why should I not marry you?
Tý-nom, tá-nom, I am not proud of course,
Tý-nom, tá-nom, the Queen is proud
Tý-nom, tá-nom, yet she married.

Translation by Eva Poš (not meant as a singing version of this song)

The voices may enter at one measure intervals, or at ♩♩ intervals. There will be some over-lapping of parts, but the challenge to sing in 8 voices is fun.
It is also possible to sing this as a 32-part canon!

Suggested accompaniments for Týnom, Tánom

Introduction and continuing ostinati

43

23. Four Shaker Songs

1. Come Dance and Sing

Come dance and sing a-

round the ring, live in love and un - ion, Dance and sing a - round the ring,

Live in sweet com - mun - ion. Sing with life, live with life, sing with life and

44

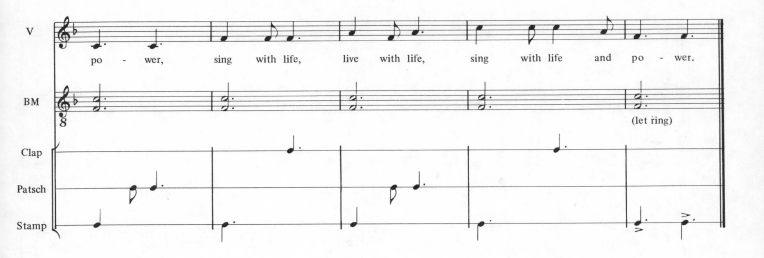

2. Simple Gifts

3. Come Life, Shaker Life

* Second voice of canon, if desired.

47

4. Hop Up and Jump Up

V: Hop up and jump up and whirl round whirl round, ga - ther love, here it is, all round, all round.

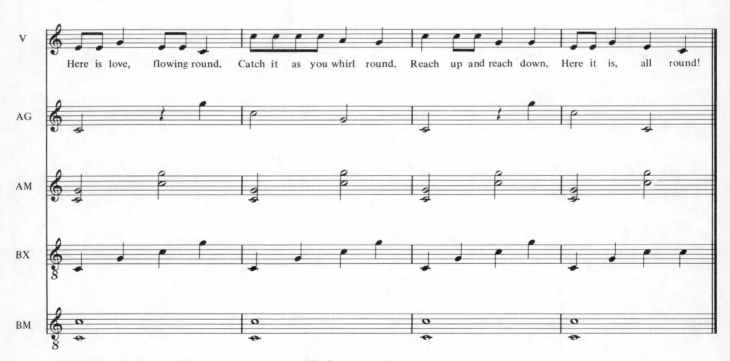

V: Here is love, flowing round. Catch it as you whirl round. Reach up and reach down, Here it is, all round!

* The piece may also be sung as a canon, with the second voice entering here.

Develop dance forms with the children, using simple steps (walking, side-galloping) and line or circle formations. Cues for appropriate movement can come from the words themselves.

24. Charlie

49

50

Make up new verses by substituting other words for "blackbird". As an interlude between repetitions of the song, let the drum (or timp) play the voice rhythm against the woodblock part as written, in a rhythmic canon. Or use a speech canon instead, before singing again. Repeat as often as you wish, substituting new words for "blackbird" each time, and end with the coda.

* The chorus must imitate exactly the inflection and voice quality of the soloist.

** Speech piece or song may be used alone.

25. Sail Away Ladies

Fiddle Song of the
Southern Mountains

2. I've got a home in Tennessee,
   Sail away ladies, sail away.
   That's the place I wanna be,
   Sail away ladies, sail away. (Chorus)

3. If ever I get my new house done,
   Sail away ladies, sail away.
   I'll give the old one to my son,
   Sail away ladies, sail away. (Chorus)

4. Come along, boys, and go with me,
   Sail away ladies, sail away.
   We'll go down to Tennessee,
   Sail away ladies, sail away. (Chorus)

26. Soldier, Soldier, Will You Marry Me?

she did go, as hard as she could run. Brought him back the

2. Off to the tail - or's she did go, as hard as she could run.

fin - est that was there _____ .

"Now sol - dier, put it on."

Brought him back the fin - est that was there _____ .

run. "Now sol - dier put them on."

"Sol - dier, sol - dier, will you mar - ry me with your

27. Improvisation With Text

Night . . . . .
And once again while I wait for you
Cold wind turns into rain. (Shiki)

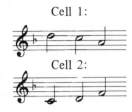

The text may be read by a single voice or a group, accompanied by the instruments. The improvisation cells may be sung, played on recorders or barred instruments, singly or in combination. Rhythmic variations of the melodic cells should be encouraged, and the melodic motifs may be inverted. The three notes of each cell should remain constant. A non-pitched percussion part will enrich the texture and allow for further improvisation experience.

"Night" from AN INTRODUCTION TO HAIKU, copyright © 1958 by Harold G. Henderson. Reprinted by permission of Doubleday & Company, Inc.

28. Two Poems

A Meeting

Right at my feet___
    and when did you get here,
      snail?
          (Issa
            translated by H.G. Henderson)

Umbara's Song

Capsizing   me   striking   me
the wind blows   hard   the sea   long stretched
between   striking   hard hitting   striking
me   dashing up   me   striking.

      (Umbara
      Australian Aborigine poem
      translated by A.W. Howitt)

29. Patsching Exercise

Example: #5 Transferred to Xylophone, accompanied by
#2 on timpani.

Examples are taken from Orff-Schulwerk "Musik für Kinder"

30. What's Old Women Made Of?

* With fingertips, sweep quietly around the drum head
  on ♩. 's; thumb plays all ♩ 's, third finger, all ♪'s.

64

accompanying patterns

2. What's old men made of, made of?
   What's old men made of?
   Pipes and smokes, and collars that chokes,
   That's what old men are made of.

   Note:
   Patterns are played twice before the verse
   begins.

accompanying patterns

3. What's little girls made of,
      made of?
   What's little girls made of?
   Sugar and spice, and every-
      thing nice,
   That's what little girls are
      made of.

   Note:
   Use ending on interlude
   before the voice enters.

accompanying patterns

4. What's little boys made of, made of?
   What's little boys made of?
   Snips and snails, and puppy dogs' tails,
   That's what little boys are made of.

accompanying patterns

5. What's little babies made
      of, made of?
   What's little babies made
      of?
   Diapers and crumbs, and
      sucking their thumbs,
   That's what little babies
      are made of.

   Note:
   The pattern comes once
   before the voice enters.

31. The Pease Branle

The Branle is an historical dance which appears in many forms: Simple, Double, Gai, Bourgogne, Official and others. "The Branle Called Pease" has been described by Thoinot Arbeau in a book called *Orchesography* which was first published in 1589 in France. Arbeau explains the dances of the time with examples of both music and steps. The music was often performed on a three-holed pipe and a drum played by one person.

The original notation of the Pease Branle looks like this:

* more color can be added to the melody by doubling the soprano recorder with a sopranino an octave higher.

** A drone of G's and D's on a stringed instrument (bowed, plucked, or struck with a beater) can be added to the accompaniment.

Branles are early line or circle dances of couples with the woman on the right of her partner. Most of the movement is sideways rather than forward or backward. The steps to the right are usually a bit smaller than those to the left so that the line or circle gradually progresses to the left.

The basic step of the Branle is a <u>double.</u> This is a step to the side, close with the other foot, step to the side, close again but without weight. This enables the dancer to begin the next double in the opposite direction. The jumps in place are from both feet and landing on both.

Double left
L,R,L,R

Double right
R,L,R,L

Man jumps (Woman waits)
(Up-Landing)

(Man waits) Woman jumps
(Up-Landing)

Man steps to L with left foot and jumps three times in place (Woman waits)

(Man waits) Woman jumps
(Up-Landing)

Man jumps (Woman waits)
(Up-Landing)

Woman steps to left with left foot and jumps three times in place (Man waits)

32. Weeping Mary

* Sing the chorus after each solo part.

68

33. An Old Story

Narratively: not fast
Recorder; whistling; singing "la"; glockenspiel; etc. choice or alternation.

This piece lends itself to pantomime.

34. Two Canons

1.

2.

Da capo Canon 1

*I₁ = Instrument 1
*I₂ = Instrument 2
One might choose glockenspiel, xylophone or recorder.

71

35. Listening to Haydn

Objectives: exploration of rhythm, texture, form

1. Teach the first four-measure phrase by rote or note.

2. Add the second four-measure phrase. The last two measures form a kind of coda to the theme. Transfer to non-pitched percussion instruments.

3. Play in canon as scored with the second voice sounding in a color which contrasts with the first.

4. Improvise a contrasting "B" section which is the same as the "A" section in length and in rhythmic feeling.

5. Listen to Haydn's Menuetto from String Quartet in D minor Op. 76 #2 (bars 1-11) and follow the treatment of the already learned "A" section contrasted with Haydn's "B".

   Can the students discover the return of "A"?
   Introduce children to score reading.

72

36. Jimmy Randal

Kentucky
Collected by John Jacob Niles

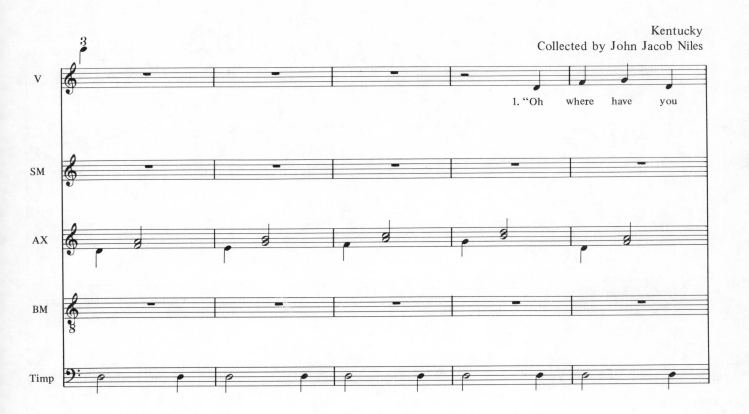

1. "Oh where have you

been Jim - my Ran - dal, my son, Oh, where have you rov - ed my

73

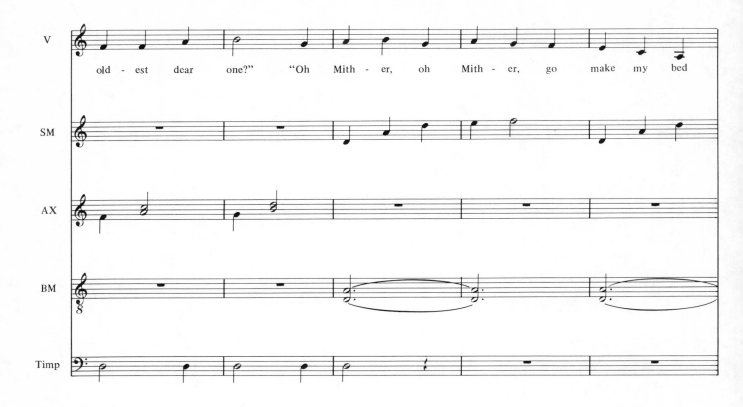

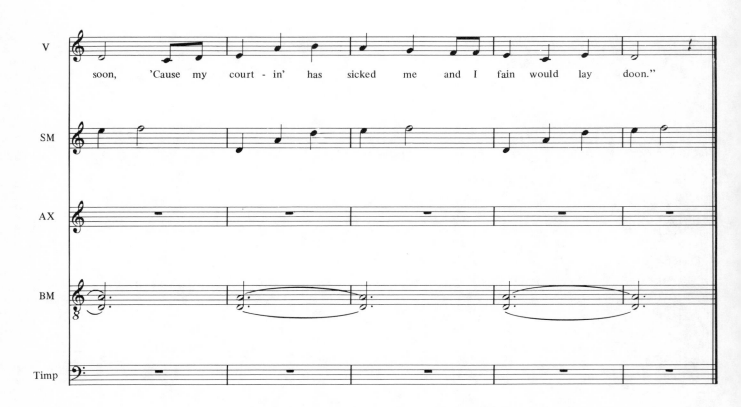

74

2.
"What had you for supper,
Jimmy Randal, my son,
What had you for supper,
my oldest dear one?"
"Some fried eels and parsnips,
go make my bed soon,
'Cause my courtin' has sicked me
and I fain would lay doon."

3.
"What will you give me
Jimmy Randal, my son,
What will you your mother,
my oldest dear one?"
"My house and my lands, Mither,
make my bed soon,
'Cause my courtin' has sicked me
and I fain would lay doon."

4.
"What will you your father,
Jimmy Randal, my son,
What will you your father,
my oldest dear one?"
"My wagon and team, Mither,
make my bed soon,
'Cause my courtin' has sicked me
and I fain would lay doon."

5.
"What will you your brother,
Jimmy Randal, my son,
What will you your brother,
my oldest dear one?"
"My horn and my hound, Mither,
make my bed soon,
'Cause my courtin' has sicked me
and I fain would lay doon."

6.
"What will you your sweetheart,
Jimmy Randal, my son,
What will you your sweetheart,
my oldest dear one?"
"Bullrushes, bullrushes,
and them all parched brown,
'Cause she gave me the pizen
That I did drink down."

7.
"And when you are dead,
Jimmy Randal, my son,
And when you are dead,
my oldest dear one?"
"Go dig me a grave side
my grandfather's son,
'Cause my courtin' has sicked me
and I fain would lay doon."

37. Danse

* With sopranino recorder ad libitum

Dance Form:

Two lines facing each other

A

Lines move toward each other with step R, step L, step-hop R, then away from each other with step L, step R, step-hop L.

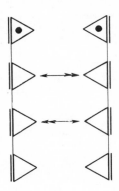

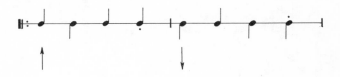

Lines move toward each other, each person changing with opposite by passing R shoulders and making a half turn in place (R,L,R,L,R, touch L, L, touch R).

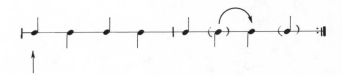

Repeat all of A — dancers will end in beginning position. (The final time, the right foot closes instead of touching.)

B

Dancers in each line join hands and are led so that the lines pass each other first at the top of the set and then at the bottom. The line that passes on the outside at the top may pass on the inside at the bottom.
Light running steps (R,L,R,L,) and step-hop R, step-hop L, is the sequence for this floor pattern.

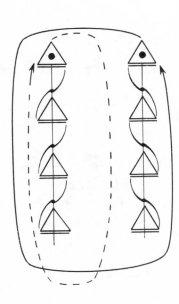

The sequence is done four times.

The dance is performed ABA. If more repetition is desired, perform ABABA etc. Possibilities for other floor patterns in the B section can also be explored.

38. A Nonsense Rondo

"Infirtaris" from THE MERRY-GO-ROUND, edited by James Reeves, Heinemann Educational Books Ltd., London.
Reprinted by permission.

B Gibberish

Mysteriously, with mock seriousness

In-fir - tar - is In - oak - none - is, In - mud - eek - are, In - clay -

none - is, Goats - eat - i - vy, Mares - eat - oats _____.

Repeat **A**

C Way Down South

Gaily

80

81

* The "Moos" are chanted, each with its own comfortable range, coming into a sustained pitch in G Pentatonic scale from below, and sliding down off it at the end with an abrupt diminuendo. Don't allow the "Moos" to overpower the tune. The cowbell plays where indicated but should sound casual, not too precise or regular, as the cows move around the meadow.

** Or improvise freely.

82

Repeat **A**

39. Big-Eye Rabbit

Southern Mountain Song

The rab-bit is the kind of thing, that

trav-els in the dark. Nev-er knows when dan-ger's near 'til he hears old Ro-ver bark.

Big - eye rab - bit, boo! boo! Big - eye rab - bit, boo!

Big - eye rab - bit, boo! boo! Big - eye rab - bit boo!

40. Follow the Leader

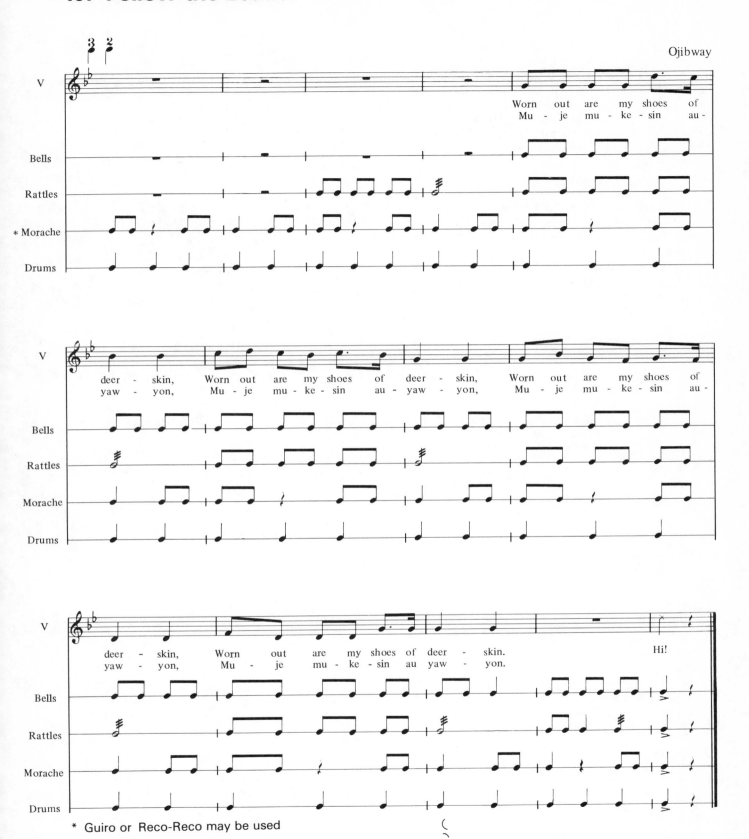

This is a children's follow-the-leader game. The followers must imitate exactly the movement, tempo, and style of the leader. The rhythm may have to be changed to match the movement, and the patterns adjusted accordingly as new leaders vary the movement and tempo to suit themselves. In skipping, for instance, the patterns would change to ♩ ♪♩ ♪♩ ♪♩ | ♩. ♩. and all the supporting patterns would adjust, etc.

Bells are tied around the dancers' ankles and will ring at every step. Each boy also carries a pair of gourd rattles, one in each hand, and plays them alternately. The drummers stand together at one side of the dance area, and both sing and play. The Morache players lean their notched sticks on resonating half gourds (or other containers), kneel in front of the drummers, and sing as they watch the game.

The leaders may use a variety of Indian dance steps, as well as the obvious motor movements and combinations of them.

1. Toe-heel step: Step on L toe on first eighth, on L heel on second eighth;
Step on R toe on third eighth, on R heel on fourth eighth, etc.
Usually in crouching position.

2. Scrape step: Toe is set forward, without weight, and immediately pulled back and weight shifted onto heel, rather like an animal pawing impatiently.

3. Modified gallop: One foot leads, and the other pushes backwards quickly, as if one were pushing a scooter.

4. Animal steps: Duck walk: squatting, with arms bent like wings.
Deer step: walking stiff-legged.
Elk leap: jumping high onto one foot. Etc.

5. Stamping step: Step L, stamp R 3 times.
Step R, stamp 3 times.

6. Marking time: Legs apart, knees and toes turned out, bounce onto heels on ♪♪♪♪

7. Jump step: Jump to L on left foot ♪, to right on R foot ♩, then on both feet, 𝅗𝅥

8. Women's step: Step L, bend knees, slide R foot beside L foot, bend knees, ♩♩♩♪

In English, the vowels correspond to the following sounds:

a = ah (father)
e = similar to e in bed (no-diphthong)
i = ee (see)
o = oh (similar to o in molest [no diphthong])
u = oo (cool)

88

41. Wade in the Water

42. Recorder Rondo

Movement suggestions

Since this is an individual dance, floor arrangement is arbitrary.

Beginning with feet together, step forward right (♩), snap (♩),
Close, bringing left foot forward to right (♩), snap (♩).

In place, step right (♩), snap (♩), step left (♩), snap (♩).
In place, step right (♩), snap (♩), step left (♩), snap (♩).

On the repeat step backward left (♩), snap (♩).
Close, bringing right foot to left (♩). Snap (♩).
In place, step right (♩), snap (♩), step left (♩), snap (♩).
In place, step right (♩), snap (♩), snap (♩).

Patsch (♩) in place during the improvisation section.

Students should be encouraged to create variations on the above movement suggestions, trying partner hand games or other body gestures to replace the snaps.

43. The Seasons —
A Rondo in Four Parts

Teaching notes:

This Rondo is made up of Haiku poems and pentatonic melodies with fairly simple ostinati. The form itself is one which children readily comprehend, especially if there has been previous experience with it. The particular challenge of this piece is in thinking ahead: What season is next? Which variation of the A section follows?

What is necessary to obtain the proper mood changes throughout?

Two of the four seasonal poems are "set" musically; the other two, Spring and Fall, are descriptive poems which sould be set by the class or a small group therein. Movement and sound possibilities abound.

It is suggested that the piece as a whole be developed over a period of four to six class sessions, so that all ideas for expanding the B, C, D, E sections may be tried out and final forms made familiar to all.

Text:

The Seasons

A		The seasons changing,
		Spring, Summer, Fall then Winter;
		Each a new rhythm.

B	Spring	Spring! Birds fill the sky.
		They soar and dive so freely.
		My dreams go with them.

C	Summer	Frogs croaking — sunlight!
		Treetops floating in the wind,
		Oh! What a morning!

D	Autumn	Leaves fall gently down.
		They are red, brown, yellow, orange.
		Crackle, Creak, Crunch, Swish.

E	Winter	Snow floats down softly,
		Covering the world in white
		Blankets full of love.

92

A. Seasons

Slow walking tempo

The sea-sons chang-ing, Spring, Sum-mer, Fall, then Win-ter; Each a new rhy-thm.

B. Spring

Spring! Birds fill the sky
They soar and dive so freely.
My dreams go with them.

A. Brisk walking tempo

The sea-sons chang-ing, Spring, Sum-mer, Fall, then Win-ter; Each a new rhy-thm.

94

D Fall

Leaves fall gently down.
They are red, brown, yellow, orange.
Crackle, Creak, Crunch, Swish.

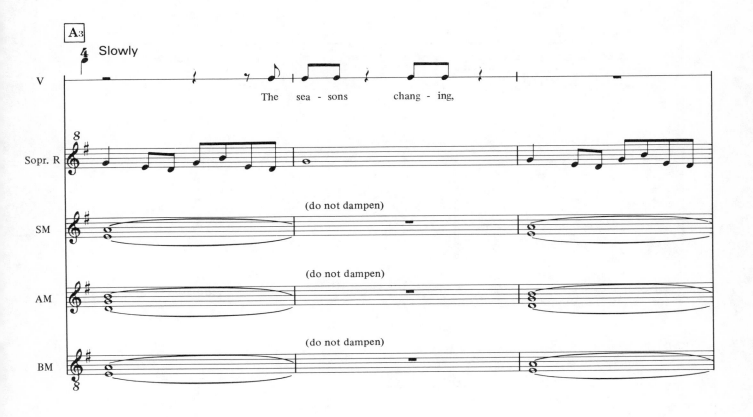

E Winter

Slow walk

* Snow floats down soft-ly   co - ver - ing the world in white   blankets full of love,

Ostinato fade; snowflakes are the last to stop.

* random snowflake-like taps on glockenspiel and finger cymbals, continue arbitrarily throughout.
** for any metallophone or resonator bells.

A₄

Slowly

The sea - sons   chang - ing.

Sopr.R

PART

2

Singing of well-known and new songs is the central activity of the music lesson. In Orff-Schulwerk the element of singing is usually combined with that of movement and of playing the instruments. One dances while singing, conducts while singing. Accompanying with instruments helps to clarify the rhythmic, metric and harmonic structure of a song and allows one to experience the music as a whole.

Instrumental playing techniques are more demanding. Children are not satisfied with playing at a level lower than the standards they have set as a result of comparisons they have made through their listening experiences. The teacher must be able to give support and guidance and provide opportunities for practice.

Reading and writing go hand in hand with making music. The results will depend on the amount of time spent with this activity. The vocabulary of notation-note values and names of notes — is of great help to teachers and children at this level. Since harmonic structure plays an important part in this section, the use of Tonic, Dominant and Subdominant, and the relation of the I-IV-V triads should be made clear to the children.

Movement is integrated with singing and instrumental playing. The folk dance repertoire is expanded.

Harmonic experiences are emphasised. In Volumes I and II and in Part I of Volume III, songs and instrumental pieces are often accompanied by a bordun. This is an early form of accompaniment using low sustained tones, usually the tonic and the fifth above.

Sometimes the fifth moves. This is called a "swinging" bordun.

Still centered upon one tone and therefore similar to bordun, are ostinato accompaniments of triads in a regularly changing pattern.

98

Because the sound of this kind of accompaniment is rich and full, it becomes a motivation for improvisation. The patterns below are recommended to accompany such melodic improvisations. Remember to change the key and meter frequently!

All ostinato forms are based on a tonal center which does not change. For this reason such accompaniments are best suited for pentatonic and modal melodies.

Diatonic melodies in major and minor are generally accompanied with chords of cadential harmonies. In this volume the major triads I-IV-V are developed through singing and playing and in tasks for improvisation and form.

44. Ostinato Exercises

- It is possible to combine several ostinati of contrasting rhythms and instrumental timbres.

- Practice the different patterns with sound gestures and find suitable non-pitched percussion instruments on which to play them.

- The ostinati can also be transferred to melodic instruments.

- There are many ways in which the combined rhythms can be structured to build small forms.

- Encourage the children to find their own ostinati, instruments and forms.

- Look for ostinato possibilities in speech and movement as well. There are ostinati in other art forms.

- Improvise melodies above the ostinati.

- Listen to selected recordings of African and Brazilian music. Try to find ostinati in other compositions as well.

I Basic Patterns:

Possible Instrumentation

Although the notation for Bongo and TB is on a single line, the distribution of pitches should be as above.

Suggestions for structuring:

II Basic Patterns:

1. Suggested instrument: Wood Block or Temple Blocks

2. Suggested instrument: Guiro

3. Suggested instrument: Hanging Cymbal

4. Suggested instrument: Tambourine

5. Suggested instrument: Bass Drum

* ♩ = strike, do not scrape

Suggestions for building a form:

- play the 6 measures Tutti
- repeat but omit measure two
- try only guiro and cymbal in measure two
- imitate the instruments with the voice — (except for Bass Drum) and try the following:

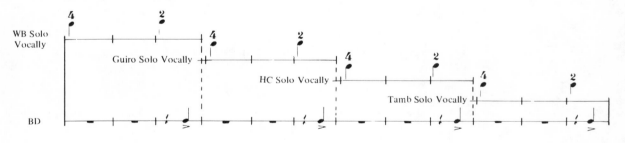

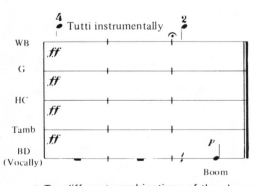

- Try different combinations of the above.

Here are four examples which show visual forms for the combining of ostinato patterns. They represent three rhythmic patterns in the form of a score. Instrumentation is open, and they can also be presented as an exercise in reading.

I.

II.

III.

IV.

The children's own creations can be notated similarly.

Children should be encouraged to make their own compositions.

III Basic Patterns:

1.

2.

3.

Possible Instrumentation:

Soprano Instruments

Alto Instruments

Bass Instruments

Transferred to melodic instruments:

S Instruments

A Instruments

B Instruments

Suggestions:

- Form three groups, for example:
  1.) Recorders and guitar
  2.) SX, AX, and BX
  3.) Non-pitched instruments

- Within each group work out a form using these ostinati.

- Bring the groups together to make a larger form which will emphasize the contrasting timbres.

- Improvise melodic phrases above the ostinati.

45. Lions

If you search for li - ons   with a wa - ry eye,   you will find that li - ons   are

ea - sy to —— spy.

(walks   soft - ly . . . .)

If you search for li - ons   with a wa - ry eye,   You will find that li - ons   are

ea - sy to —— spy.

(State - ly, mag - ni - fi - cent . . . .)

105

If you search for li - ons with a wa-ry eye, you will find that li - ons are

ea - sy to —— spy.

(See his head held high)

If you search for li - ons with a wa-ry eye, You will find that li - ons are

(Strolls through the jun - gle)

ea - sy to spy.

If you search for li - ons with a wa - ry eye, you will find that li - ons are

ea - sy to spy.

(not hard to tell - - - - -)

ea - sy to —— spy.   Yah!

46. The Good Old Man

1. Where are you go - ing, my good old man? Where are you go - ing, my hon-ey, my love? Best old soul in the world. *Going to the store.* *

2. What are you going to buy, my good old man?
   What are you going to buy, my honey, my love?
   Best old soul in the world.
   New dress.

3. How much will it cost? etc.
   Fifty cents.

4. What do you want for supper? etc.
   Sack of potatoes.

5. Potatoes will kill you. etc.
   Don't care; want to die anyhow.

6. Where do you want to be buried? etc.
   In the chimney-corner.

7. Ashes'll fall on you. etc.
   Don't care if they do, so I'm close to you.

* Words in italics are spoken.

From ENGLISH FOLK SONGS FROM THE SOUTHERN APPALACHIANS, Cecil Sharp, by permission of Oxford University Press

47. Dundai

Theme with variations

Hebrew Dance

Da Capo ad libitum

111

VAR. 1.

VAR. 2.

112

VAR. 3.

* or an assortment of small percussion ad lib.

Dance Form: (Theme only)

A circle, holding hands in low position, arms hanging

[A] section: Two "grapevine" steps clockwise. (Starting with feet together. R crosses in front of L, step to L with L foot, R crosses behind L, step to L with L foot)

Step-hop R ↑, Step-hop L ↓, four steps in place — R, L, R, L —

Repeat all of [A] section.

[B] section: Four "drměs" steps counterclockwise. (Step to R with R foot keeping knee straight, L foot crosses in front of R with knee slightly bent.

Dropping hands, turn in place clockwise with four steps (R,L,R,L) then two steps in place bending knee slightly after each step. (R, bend R, L, bend L.)

Repeat all of [B] section.

[A]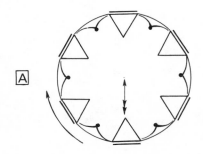

[B]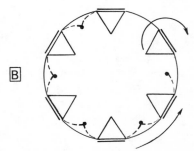

114

48. Never a Child as He
(Canon)

1. Ne - ver so love - ly a child __ as He,

Born in a stab - le so low - ly; Born of a vir - gin, King to be,

Ne - ver a child —— so love - ly.

2. An - gels were sing - ing and shep herds did pray. Wise - men were bring - ing their

2. An - gels were sing - ing and

116

3. Here Gods' own Son, lay asleep on the hay,
   Here angels sang of his glory;

Jesus our savior, born today,
Jesus, the Lord and the Master.

49. Oh, Jerusalem

V: Oh, Je - ru - sa - lem _____ Sweet lit - tle

V: ba - by born ___ in a sta - ble, Oh, Je - ru - s'lem in the

V: morn _____

50. The Mysterious Cat

122

123

3. I saw a cat — 'twas but a dream,
   Who scorned the slave that brought her cream—
   Mew, mew, mew.
   Did you ever hear of a thing like that?
   Oh, what a proud mysterious cat.
   Mew, mew, mew.

4. Unless the slave were dressed in style,
   And knelt before her all the while.
   Mew, mew, mew.
   Did you ever hear of a thing like that?
   Oh, what a proud mysterious cat.
   Mew, mew, mew.

51. Compositions

A. Warm-up

1. While the teacher plays various wind-like sounds, e.g. scratching a drumhead, shaking a tambourine, playing glissandi on a piano or xylophone, the class moves through space as the wind, according to the sounds.

2. This time, as the teacher plays, each one becomes an object of the wind's force; a tree, cloud, flower, blade of grass, paper, etc.
3. Half the class moves as the wind, the other half as its objects; players are chosen to make wind sounds on the instruments.

Night Wind

Wise is the wind that ush-ers in the night. Gen-tle is the breeze, in-
vis-i-ble from sight. Oh, night wind sur-round me and take me far a-
way. Oh, let me dream un-til the dawn of day.

B. "Night Wind"

1. Seated, the class sways to the pulse as it listens to the song.
2. The class discusses the song's melodic structure in terms of question and answer, small phrase similarities and overall form.
3. The small melodic phrases are echoed on "lai" and expressed with had movements.
4. The words are also learned by echo-singing.
5. Each person experiments, finding a movement for the similar phrases which expresses both the melodic feeling and words.
6. Each person combines the movements to fit the form of the song, as everyone sings the song.
7. The group divides in half and discusses the use of group space.
8. While one group sings and watches, the other performs, using the determined spatial structure and the individual movements.
9. It can also be performed without singing, but with alto recorder, or silently.

52. Instrumental ABA

126

In this instrumental piece for barred instruments the tonality alternates between a minor and C major. The soprano xylophone has the melody in the A section and in the B section the alto glockenspiel has the melody for the first four measures, the alto xylophone for the second four measures. The music might also provide a stimulus for dance improvisation.

53. Oh, Suzanna

(Dance to a well-known Stephen Foster song)

Form: Circle of partners, e.g. green (boys) and orange (girls). *

A All the greens walk three steps toward the center (R, L, R), touch L on the fourth count, and walk four steps back to place (L, R, L, R). Oranges do the same (Fig. 1).

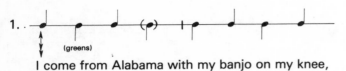

1.

(greens)

I come from Alabama with my banjo on my knee,

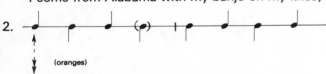

2.

(oranges)

I'm goin' to Louisiana my true love for to see.

(Fig. 1)

B Partners face each other in line of circle to begin grand right and left (Fig. 2). After giving R hand to partner and passing by him, L hand is given to the next person as he is passed, and so on. In this figure, the seventh person you meet becomes your new partner. Keeping hold of R hands, the people facing clockwise turn so that both partners are facing counterclockwise in promenade position (R hand holding R, L holding L, usually with the R arms crossing above the L).

3.

Hands R _____ L _____ R _____ L _____

It rained all night the day I left, the weather it was dry,

4.

R _____ L _____ R _____

The sun so hot, I froze to death, Suzanna, don't you cry.

(Fig. 2)

C Partners promenade counterclockwise sixteen steps (Fig. 3) All end this sequence facing the center to begin the dance again.

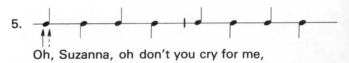

5.

Oh, Suzanna, oh don't you cry for me,

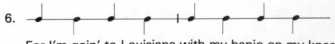

6.

For I'm goin' to Louisiana with my banjo on my knee.

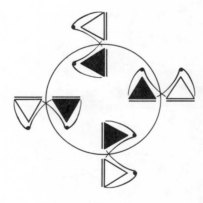

(Fig. 3)

* Sometimes it isn't possible to have boys and girls pair off (e.g., when there isn't an equal number of each). Then you can use 2 colors or 2 of some other category.

128

54. Developing Chord Changes (I-V-I)

1. Finding melodies for a given bass

Children should be encouraged to improvise short melodies above a bass line that changes from tonic to dominant. It is best to begin with the timpani as the accompanying instrument, but one may include the bass xylophone and bass metallophone as well. If there is a string bass or cello available, the ensemble sound and clarity of the bass line will be strengthened. The remaining melodic instruments in the ensemble, including voice and recorder, should be used for making up the tunes.

In a large group, choose three or four children to make a melodic improvisation while the others play or sing the tonic-dominant accompaniment. One child can conduct the proper I-V changes with hand signs for *do* and *so* or merely by showing the different pitch levels. Constant changing of parts should give each child a chance to try the bass, a melody, conducting.

At first the improvising of melodies to the given bass may be a matter of trial and error until a feeling for the dominant is secure. It is necessary to choose examples which have a clearly defined bass line.

As improvisation skills develop, try alternating between two tonalities. This will help maintain interest and concentration when exercises become too repetitive.

Examples

A bass accompaniment in C major

A sample melody over the given bass

The same material transposed to F major

Using the same bass, have four children improvise one after the other. The first — C major, the second — F major, the third back to C, and the fourth, F. Then change players.

129

Here are some sample bass lines over which to improvise melodies.

2. Finding the bass for a given melody

As with all exercises which introduce new musical elements, this one should begin with examples which clearly state the need for cadential harmonies. Again it is the task of the children to find the suitable accompaniment. The deepest instruments in the ensemble should be used for playing the tonic and dominant of the chosen tonality (Timpani, bass xylophone, bass metallophone, string bass or cello if available).

Proper mallet technique for all instruments should be developed in this exercise. Alternating hands, and if necessary, playing consecutive notes with the same hand to avoid awkward movement from tonic to dominant and back, is important. The children should try to work out the "handing" themselves.

Example: A given melody

Possible accompaniments

Here is an example of smooth "sticking" for the suggested bass 2 above:

55. Fod

American folksong
Oklahoma

V SX: I went down to the mow-in' field. Too - rye - too - rye Fa - da - link - a - die - do.

V SX: I went down to the mow - in' field, FOD! I went down to the

V SX: mow - in' field, And a big black snake came and bit my heel, Too - rye - de - day

2. Sat on a stump to take my rest Too-rye etc.
   there I saw a woodchuck on his nest. . . .

3. (The) woodchuck grinned to my banjo song
   up came a skunk with his britches on. . . .

4. Woodchuck, skunk, got into a fight
   Smelled so band, they put out the light. . . .
   (or "fought so hard")

The following sound gesture pattern may be used as an introduction or as an ostinato to accompany the singing:

clap
stamp

5. Danced and played 'til the chimney' 'gan to rust (3)
   Hard to tell who smelt (looked) the wust. . . .
   (Repeat first verse, ending on "Fod"!)

131

56. Black Eyed Susie

2. All I want to make me happy,
   Two little boys to call me Pappy.
   Refrain

3. Love my wife and love my baby,
   Love my bisquits sopped in gravy.
   Refrain

57. Cumberland Reel

Form: Longways set in which the head couple ends up at the bottom, so that each couple has a turn being at the head. As you face the head of the set, (traditionally where the music is located), the man has his partner on his R. As the dance begins, the lines are facing each other (Fig. 1).

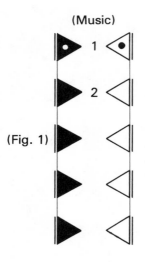

(Music)

(Fig. 1)

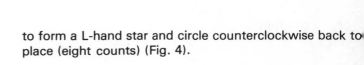

(Fig. 2)

(Fig. 3)

to form a L-hand star and circle counterclockwise back to place (eight counts) (Fig. 4).

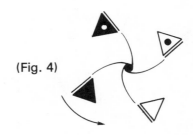

(Fig. 4)

A Couples 1 and 2 form a R-hand star and circle clockwise (eight counts) (Fig. 2).

Each person makes half-turn inwards (Fig. 3)

A₁ Head couple slides (side-gallop) down the set holding both hands (eight counts) and back up the set to place (eight counts, (Fig. 5).

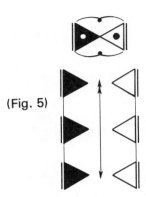

(Fig. 5)

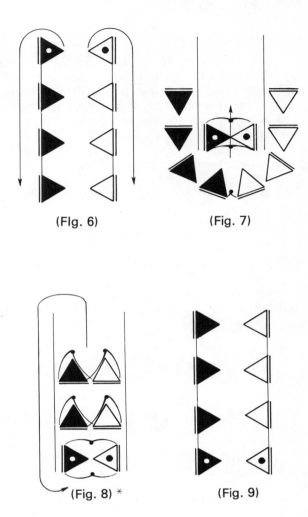

(Flg. 6)   (Fig. 7)

(Fig. 8) *   (Fig. 9)

B Head couple casts off and leads down the outside of the set with the lines following (Fig. 6). When couple 1 reaches the bottom of the set, they form an arch for the others to go through (Fig. 7). Second couple now leads in a promenade* up the set, turns to the L, down the L of the set, and back up again to place (Fig. 8) (thirty-two counts). Second couple now becomes the head couple for the next turn of the dance (Fig. 9).

* In promenade position, partners hold R hand in R hand, L in L. Usually R hand of man crosses over L of his partner.

58. Working with Poetry

In attempting to combine poetry and music, one might begin either with a given poem or by encouraging children to write their own poems. It is probably easier to start with examples of poetry accompanied in various ways by musical sounds in order to provide some good models.

The following are three examples:

1. A very simple treatment of a child's poem

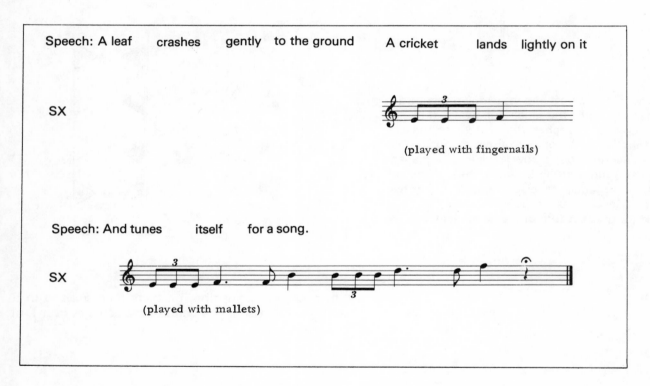

MIRACLES — Poems by Children of the English-speaking World, collected by Richard Lewis. Reprinted by permission of SIMON & SCHUSTER, a Division of Gulf and Western Corp.

2. A percussion accompaniment for a poem with a lot of rhythmic energy,

The Pickety Fence

* A combination of differently pitched claves and wood-
blocks may be substituted for temple blocks.

3. An example using speech, singing, and melodic instruments

April Rain Song

59. Poems

Poor old Jonathan Bing.
Went out on his carriage to visit the king.
But everyone pointed and said, "Look at that!
Jonathan Bing has forgotten his hat!"

Good night Mr. Beetle,
Good night Mr. Fly,
Good night Mrs. Ladybug,
The moon's in the sky.

Good night, Miss Kitten,
Good night Mr. Pup.
I'll see you in the morning
When the sun comes up.

I don't know why the sky is blue
Or why the raindrops splatter through.
Or why the grass is wet with dew,
Do you?
Do you?

There once was a witch of Willoby Wood,
And a weird, wild witch was she.
With hair that was snarled
and hands that were gnarled.
And a kickety, rickety knee.

60. Ersatz Liadl

The title means: a substitute or "made-up" song. The word Liadl is Austrian dialect for the German: Lied. Try to play the piece one tone higher after learning it in the original key.

Small percussion may be added *ad libitum*. Try to find a dance form suitable to the music.

140

61. Praised Be the Lord

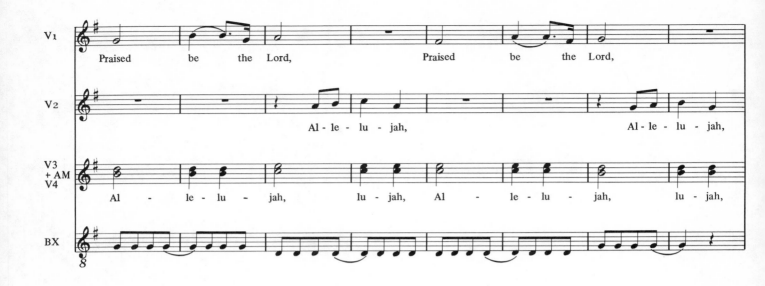

62. All 'Round the Ring

The following lesson was developed by a group of teachers to illustrate the use of different media with the same basic material. Speech and vocal, as well as instru-mental, ostinato patterns were created to demonstrate color possibilities. Some movement and teaching sug-gestions are included.

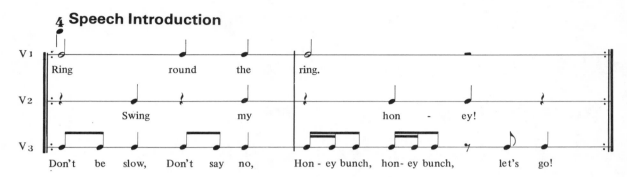

Instrumental Setting

144

Movement Suggestions

1. Partners in a circle.
   Measures 1-4: Circle left.
   Measures 5-6, 7-8, 9-10: Face partner:

   patsch clap clap partner's hand

   Measures 11-12: Swing partner.

2. Circle mixer.
   Measures 1-4: Circle moving left, with one person who is "it" (the honeybunch) inside circle moving right.
   Measures 5-10: All stop and clap the beat in place, except "it", who continues to move. On the last "honeybunch" "it" stops by the person closest to him.
   Measures 11-12: "It" and partner swing and the partner becomes the new "it".

Teaching Suggestions

1. Clap this rhythm from notation:

2. Place the last beat at the beginning of the pattern. Find this phrase in the song.

3. Compare the rhythm of the last phrase to the others in the song. Notate from children's suggestions. Discover and notate the duration of the last note.

4. Sight sing the following three motives. Find them in the song.

63. El Tren por Almendral
The Train to Santa Fe

Argentina

Choo - choo _____ choo - choo _____

THE GAME: The class kneels in a circle with knees almost touching. Each player holds a shoe, a small stone, or a block of wood in his right hand. At every "X" the shoe is passed to the neighbor on the left, precisely on the beat, and exactly in front of his right knee. At "chi-que, chi-que", each player pretends to pass the shoe, placing it in front of his left neighbor's right knee as usual and then moving it back in front of his own right knee before letting go of it on the final "cha" (or "che"). Players who miss are eliminated one by one and appointed policeman to watch for the the next mistakes. The tempo is gradually increased as the game is repeated until only the winner (or a small group of winners) is left. When the game is familiar, it may also be played backwards, from left to right.

NOTE: The accompanying parts, including the extra voice parts, may be used in various combinations during the many repetitions of the song, — or, indeed, omitted entirely. More parts may be added as players are eliminated, so that the orchestra grows as the number of players diminishes. The game itself proves so engrossing to players and watchers alike that it may be difficult to find any players at all.

64. Saeynu

Traditional Israeli

Li li li li li   li li   li   li   li.

65. Creole Tune

A sprightly tune to play on the recorder, another instrument, or sing... and then invent a movement form for it....

How do you want your form to begin? Consider these shapes and experiment getting into them:

What kinds of contrasting patterns can you form for B ?.

The harmonic scheme might work in the following way for A :

How might you expand this into a faster, more jubilant accompaniment? Can you thicken the texture by adding more instruments using this same harmonic pattern but a different, complimentary rhythm?

Can you keep B quite open by comparison by only playing in unison, but invent a lovely instrumental sound to happen on the rests?

66. Broom Man

Street Cry

"The Broom Man" from A BOOK OF BALLADS, SONGS AND SNATCHES, selected by Haig and Regina Shekerjian,
Arranged for Piano with Guitar Chords by Robert De Cormier. Copyright © 1966 by Haig and Regina Shekerjian.

152

67. Shifting Accents

B Speak with accented consonant sounds: conduct in four while speaking to visualize the shift in accented syncopation pattern.

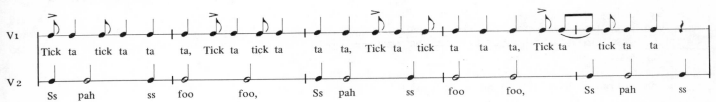

Tick ta tick ta ta ta, Tick ta tick ta ta ta, Tick ta tick ta ta ta, Tick ta tick ta ta

Ss pah ss foo foo, Ss pah ss foo foo, Ss pah ss

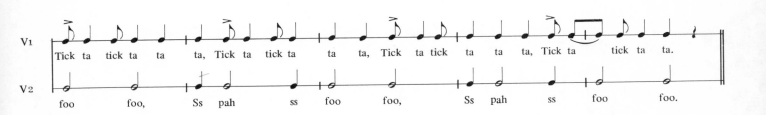

Tick ta tick ta ta ta, Tick ta tick ta ta ta, Tick ta tick ta ta ta, Tick ta tick ta ta.

foo foo, Ss pah ss foo foo, Ss pah ss foo foo.

A (voice second time only)

La la la la la la la la la la la, La la la la la la la la la la.

Students will recognize the motive, ♪♩ ♪♩ ♩ , as 'Flashing like silver' from the familiar "My Paddle's Keen and Bright". Conduct together in the traditional four beat pattern and speak the pattern as indicated in B . By adding one pulse, the syncopation shifts over one beat each time it is repeated. The contrasting part is an augmentation of the motive. When the patterns are mastered, write them out, numbering each measure. Refer to the written example when identifying the syncopated patterns of the pitched orchestration.

Add a simple dance to A . Step on the right foot and dip, left foot and dip, and then continue to step forward right, left, right. Pivot a quarter turn left on the right foot, fourth count, second measure. Repeat the eight-beat sequence of steps, beginning with the left foot. When the sequence is repeated four times a square is outlined.

68. Gustaf's Skoal

Form: Square of 4 couples.

Couples 1 and 3 are head couples.

Couples 2 and 4 are side couples.

A Head couples take three steps toward each other, bow on the fourth count, and take four steps back to place. Side couples do the same. The sequence is repeated. It is done with a mock dignity (Fig. 1).

A toast we pledge to Gustaf who is brave and true.

A toast we pledge to Gustaf brave and true.

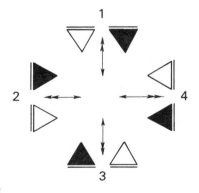

(Fig. 1)

155

B Side couples each form arches by joining inside hands and raising them. Head couples skip to center, and each person makes a quarter turn toward the nearer arch (Fig. 2). They continue skipping through arch and back to place where they swing clockwise holding both hands. The head couples then form arches for the side couples to skip through (Fig. 3). This action is done with lightness and fun. When there are more people than are needed for the dance, they can "steal" a partner as the skipping is being done.

Skipping:

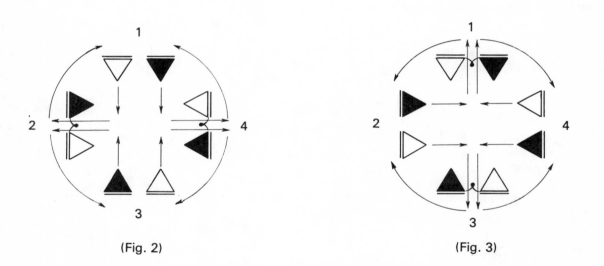

(Fig. 2)   (Fig. 3)

69. Cinquain

An easy poetic form for beginners is the cinquain. As its name indicates, it is a five line poem, the first line consisting of one word which states the theme of the poem. The second line contains two words which describe the theme; the third line has three words which must show some kind of movement; the fourth line consists of four words which describe a feeling or emotion. The fifth line contains, like the first, only one word, and it must be a synonym for the theme word. The rules may be interpreted strictly or less strictly.

Summary:

line 1—1 word, theme
line 2—2 words, descriptive
line 3—3 words, movement
line 4—4 words, feeling
line 5—1 word, synonym for theme

Examples:

Ghosts	Winter
Ghastly ghouls	Whirling drifts
Floating, flying, fleeing	Moulding snow hills
Go scare some other	Try to last all
Soul	Season

Experimenting with the cinquain form: make up a cinquain as a group project, deciding together on an accompaniment; or divide the class into groups of four to seven to work out a cinquain and to experiment with different ways to accompany it. It is simpler if the children have a common theme to write about, such as Halloween or winter.

Some guidelines for the accompaniments: keep them simple and transparent. The sounds are meant to enhance, not to overshadow, the poetry. When in doubt about adding a sound, it is usually better to leave it out.

70. Old Walt

At a leisurely speed and without a sense of hurry

Old Walt Whit - man went find - ing and seek - ing, Find - ing less than sought. Seek - ing more than found.

* With a large group, the triangle part adds a bit of "spice".
When working with smaller numbers, the part should be arranged so that it is less busy, possibly on the first and fourth beats of each measure only.

158

71. Riding Round the Cattle

162

163

Verse
solo or small group.
B
Fine
V
SX
BX or Guitar ad lib.
Snap Clap
Patsch R L
WB or Coconut Shells G
Bongo R L
p
1. I went out a rid - ing a round - ing up the cat - tle, And I thought I would be a rid - ing up strad - dle,
2. Went out a rid - ing and a I got a strad - dle, And the mule throwed me right back off of the sad - dle,
3. My foot in the stir - rup my seat in the sad - dle, I'm the best lit - tle cow - boy that ev - er rode strad - dle
4. With my blan - kets, and my slick - er and my raw - hide rope, I'm a slid - ing down the trail in a long keen lope,
5. It's cloud - y in the west and look - ing like rain, And my darned old slick - er's in the wag - on a gain,
6. I woke up one morn - ing on the Old Chis - holm Trail, With a rope in my hand and a cow by the tail,
7. I'm up ev ery morn - ing be - fore day - light, And be - fore I sleep the moon shines bright,
d d a a d d a a d d a a d d a

NOTE: The guitar may be substituted for BX in the verses, or used in addition to vary the texture. New body-rhythm patterns may be improvised for the different verses as well, with or without the bongos, or new patterns with the coconut shells or guiro may be inserted for variety.

72. Developing Chord Changes (I-IV-V-I)

Play, sing, write and read.

Soprano and Alto instruments complete the triads.

Improvise melodies over these suggested bass accompaniments and complete the harmonies as in examples 4,
5 and 6.

73. Dashing Away with the Smoothing-Iron

V

1. a - wash - ing of
2. a - hang - ing out
3. a - starch - ing of
look'd so neat and nim - ble, O, 4. an - iron - ing of her lin - en, O, Dash - ing a - way with the
5. a - fold - ing of
6. an - air - ing of
7. a - wear - ing of

SG

AX₁

AX₂

Bass

V

Smooth - ing iron. dash - ing a - way with the smooth - ing iron she stole my heart a - way ___.

SG

AX₁

AX₂

Bass

74. Lullaby

75. Banuwah

Introduction and Coda

Liberian Folk Song

76. Sun Magic

172

77. Janie Mama

* In the bongo drum part the left and right handing has been given. It is up to the player to choose when the high or the low drum is to be played. It is for this reason that no pitch indication has been given.

177

78. A Writing Lesson Expanded

1. The first task is for the children to construct descriptive sentences:
   —adjectives
   —an interesting verb that implies some subtle locomotion
   —a prepositional phrase
   —a resolution to the action in the final clause.

   (the task requirements may differ according to the experiences of the children involved)

   EXAMPLE: THE VERY LARGE ELEPHANT LUMBERED OUT OF THE FOREST and came to rest on the top of an unoccupied tent.

   THE RED SPORTS CAR, DARTING AND WEAVING, MADE ITS WAY THROUGH THE TRAFFIC and suddenly screeched to a halt at a gas station.

2. When five good examples have been written, divide the class into 5 groups. Cut the sentences in two, placing the front ends in one hat and the back ends in another.

3. The task will now be to draw a "front" and a "back" from each hat, the results probably being zany, and to invent a short drama around the idea. This vignette should include something sung, a little movement and any instruments needed for musical accompaniment or sound effects.

   (The groups should have had some previous experience working independently in small groups.)

79. May Song

This makes a very effective drum canon. All the accented words or syllables are played with the thumb 2 or 3 inches up from the bottom rim; unaccented syllables are played with the fingers at the upper rim.

80. It is the Tears of the Earth

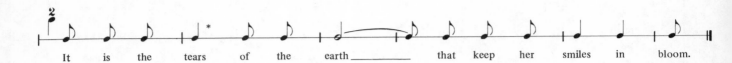

It is the tears of the earth _____ that keep her smiles in bloom.

1. Add an introduction and a coda using words from the text. One possibility might be "tears, smiles" spoken in an unmetered style by two contrasting voice groups.

2. Change the meter from duple to triple. Add a spoken ostinato such as

    tears, smiles, earth - shine

3. Use the text for movement development. The contrast of contract and expand is one possibility for exploration.

4. Use the text as a basis for color exploration on both pitched and non-pitched instruments.

5. Perform the text in canon.
   (* indicates second voice entry).

6. Let the children sing improvised melodies.

Stray Birds, # 4, from COLLECTED POEMS AND PLAYS of Rabindranath Tagore (Copyright 1916 by Macmillan Publishing Co, Inc., renewed 1944 by Rathindranath Tagore). Used by permission of Macmillan, London and Basingstroke, publishers.

81. A Hand Was Fill'd

V: A hand was fill'd with morn - ing col - ored light

V: Reach - ing for a hand.

82. Baby Song of the Four Winds

83. A Little Nonsense

1. The Crocodile

If you should meet a crocodile,
   Don't take a stick to poke him;
Ignore the welcome in his smile,
   Be careful not to stroke him.
For as he sleeps upon the Nile,
   He thinner gets and thinner;
And whene'er you meet a crocodile
   He's ready for his dinner.

2. Kilkenny Cats

There once were two cats of Kilkenny
Each thought there was one cat too many;
   So they fought and they fit,
   And they scratched and they bit,
   Till, excepting their nails
   And the tips of their tails,
Instead of two cats there weren't any.

4. The Peacock

The peacock has a score of eyes,
   With which he cannot see;
The codfish has a silent sound,
   However that may be;

No dandelions tell the time,
   Although they turn to clocks;
Cat's cradle does not hold the cat,
   Nor foxglove fit the fox.

5.

'The time has come, the Walrus said,
'To talk of many things.
Of shoes.. and ships..
   and sealing wax,
Of cabbages and kings.

3. Similar Cases

There was once a little animal
   No bigger than a fox,
And on five toes he scampered
   Over Tertiary rocks.
They called him Eohippus,
   And they called him very small,
And they thought him of no value
   (When they thought of him at all);
For the lumpish Dinoceras
   And Coryphodont so slow
Were the heavy aristocracy
   In days of long ago.

Said the little Eohippus:
   "I am going to be a horse,
And on my middle finger nails
   To run my earthly course;
I'm going to have a flowing tail,
   I'm going to have a mane,
I'm going to stand fourteen hands high
   On the psychozoic plain."
The Coryphodont was horrified,
   The Dinoceras was shocked;
And they chased young Eohippus,
   But he skipped away and mocked.

Then they laughed enormous laughter,
   And they groaned enormous groans,
And they bade young Eohippus
   Go and view his father's bones.
Said they: "You always were as small
   And mean as now we see,
And therefore it is evident
   That you're always going to be."
"What! Be a great, tall, handsome beast
With hoofs to gallop on?
Why, you'd have to change your nature!"
   Said the Loxolophodon.

They considered him disposed of,
   And retired with gait serene,
That was the way they argued
   In the early Eocene.

84. Refugee in America

* 2 part canon

All day _____ every day.
You would _____ know why.

Coda

185

85. Shabat Shalom

La   la   la   la   la   la la   la la   la,

For Jewish people the Sabbath begins at sundown on Friday evening. People greet each other on the joyful occasion by saying, "Sabbath Peace to You" (In Hebrew: Shabat Shalom)

A dance form can be developed in keeping with the character of the text and music.

86. Developing Chord Changes in Minor (I-IV-V-I, with and without leading tone)

Play, sing, write, read, complete triads, and improvise melodies over:

a) Dominant as minor triad (without leading tone)

1.

Soprano + Alto Instruments

Bass Instruments

Complete

Complete

S + A Instruments

B Instruments

2.

b) Dominant (with leading tone)

3.

S + A Instruments

B Instruments

87. Go Down, Moses

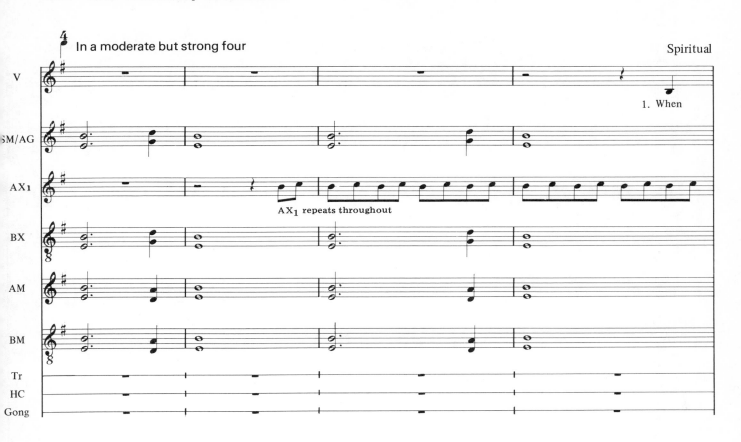

AX₁: continues pattern throughout   SX: enters on Verse 3, doubling AX₁
AX₂: enters on Verse 2 and continues   AX₃: enters on Verse 4

193

195

4. The dev - il thought he had us fast, Let my peo - ple go. But we

196

tell __ ole _____ Phar - aoh _____ to let my peo - ple go.

88. Have a Music Olympics

. . . complete with student judges grading the entrants from one to ten. The events: rhythm reading, singing, recorder playing, melody finishing, identifying masterworks on record, movement to music, improvising a melody. Sign up for your favorite event. If you'd like to represent a country other than the U.S., better look up its flag and have it handy for the parade. I wonder if the class next door would like to compete. . . .

PART
3

Singing includes songs with a variety of scales.

      a) pentatonic, pentachordal and hexatonic in different modes
      b) major
      c) minor
      d) modal (dorian, phrygian, lydian, mixolydian, aeolian)
      e) extended tonalities (from a casual use of non-diatonic to free tonal phrases)

Improvisational and compositional exercises are included to help children internalize new textures, tone colors, scales and formal structures. The texts are challenging to the children whose emotional responses are growing. Speech and singing activities are selected with this in mind.

Rhythmic exercises use less familiar patterns and meters. Patience and a kind of systematic approach can help to overcome some of the difficulties which will be encountered. The ability to cope with rhythmic and metric activities is not equal among children and some of them will not be able to do the material presented in this part.

Instrumental playing tasks have increased. Pieces and accompaniments require a variety of dynamic techniques. Occasionally it may be necessary to prepare the instrumental parts with only a few skilled players.

Movement or dramatic response is called for in many of the examples. The teacher must help to find the way which leads from the "wanting to" to the "being able to"; between the idea and the realisation of the idea. Teachers should help with preparatory exercises and guidance. Children should be given the opportunity to see and hear artistic performances.

Listening examples are referred to more frequently in Part 3. The teacher can play for the children or prepare recorded examples for such purposes (See article: "Listening: A Participatory Approach" page 328). It is important, especially in elementary music, to combine making music and listening in an active way.

89. Boomba

Episode from a Brazilian Dance

The introduction consists of the following rhythmic motifs. They may
be used singly or in combination throughout the piece.

Bring out   the big   bull   Boom - ba,

Boom - ba   la   Bam - ba.

90. Changing Meter Dance

205

Movement Suggestions

A (Moving clockwise in a circle, hands joined)

skip step step   skip   skip   skip   skip step step   skip close

Repeat steps counterclockwise

B (Moving toward center of circle, hands joined)

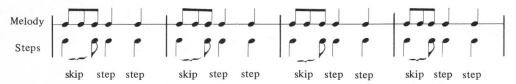

skip step step   skip step step   skip step step   skip step step

Repeat steps going backwards

A Repeat as above

206

91. "Handing" Exercise

In the following exercises for pairs of instruments or instruments played with two sticks, (bongos, congas, wood blocks, timpani, snare drum, and also two xylophone bars) it is the task of teachers and children to solve the problem of "handing". Left and right hands should be used in alternation to avoid awkward hand crossing which might interrupt the rhythmic or melodic flow. It is possible that in certain rhythmic situations the hands cannot be alternated. Sometimes the solution is only a question of which hand starts! Proper "handing" should also be considered even when rhythmic examples are spontaneously improvised.

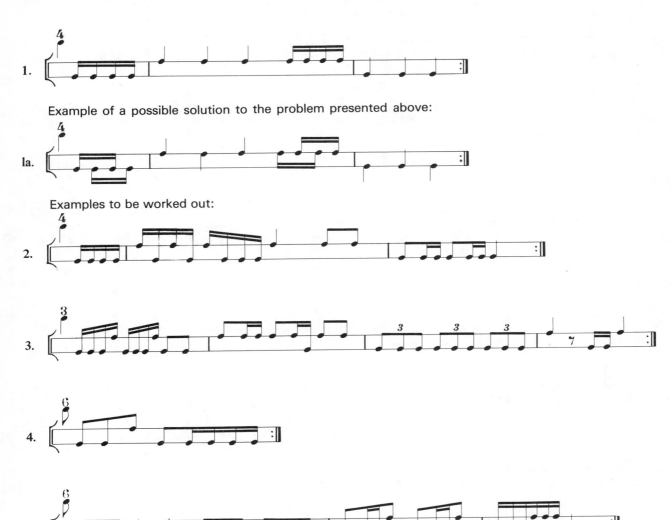

1.

Example of a possible solution to the problem presented above:

1a.

Examples to be worked out:

2.

3.

4.

5.

The notation above indicates two pitches, high and low. Example 1a. shows left hand notation with downward stems and right hand notation with upward stems.

Handing problems also occur with instruments which have no pitch differentiation, such as a snare drum or a single wood block. Notation is then presented on a single line as follows:

Ex. 2 above:

92. Water Come-a Me Eye

209

93. Puppets to Polished Performance

"Everyone please bring in a puppet and let's talk. I'll write down or tape what you say as you do, and you all can be thinking how we're going to get all these puppets going in a story-line direction..."

This was the very loose beginning which reaped a fine and formal Thanksgiving play with a group of 11 year olds. ... a "king" puppet became England's authority with recorder fanfare. ... "We Want Our Rights" became the cry of the English citizens, later set to music by the children

by the 4th grade

We want our rights we want our rights, We want our free - dom

to be free we'll move to a dif - fer - ent coun - try And lead a bet - ter life.

The animal puppets which had been brought in paralleled the story with a lion terrorizing his animal subjects. A Giles Gibbs fife tune became the interlude between the short scenes during which a squirrel puppet carried a scene sign. The decision to leave England was reached by the people and the animals who shared a ride in a one-dimensional, stick-puppet Mayflower.

See what clevernesses your children's puppets might provoke!

94. The Rose Tree

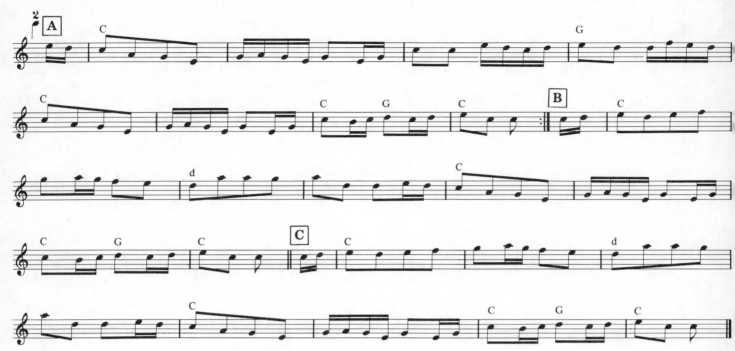

Rose Tree Contra

Form: Longways set "for as many as will." This is a *duple minor,* typical of dances in England and New England. This term refers to the sub-sets of two couples within the set as a whole. It is a *progressive* dance, meaning that every time the dance is done, each couple "1" dances with a different couple "2". The quickest way to determine each couples' number is to make circles of four from the top of the set: those facing down the set are couple "1's", those facing up the set are couple "2's". (Fig. 1) Those who are couple "1's" remain "1's" as they progress down the set until they reach the bottom. At this point, a couple "1" loses one turn (having no "2" to dance with) and rejoins the dance the next time as a couple "2". Those who are couple "2's" are progressing up the set at the same time. When each couple "2" reaches the top of the set, they lose one turn and come back into the dance as couple "1". It is traditional that the top of the set be nearest the music and that new-comers to a set being formed (or already formed) join at the bottom of the set.

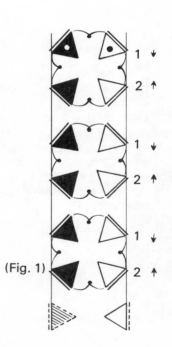

(Fig. 1)

212

The basic step is a lively walk.

A Each man "1" joins **R** hands with his lady "2", and they turn once around clockwise and "fall back" to place (eight counts). They then make a counterclockwise turn by joining **L** hands (eight counts). Each lady "1" does the same sequence with her man "2", first **R** hands (eight counts), then **L** (eight counts) (Fig. 2).

C With **R** nips together and using the inside foot as a pivot, everyone swings clockwise with his partner (sixteen counts). A common hand-hold is each person's **L** hand on his partner's **R** shoulder and **R** hand on **L** side of partner's waist. Another possibility is holding both hands. You can take advantage of momentum by leaning away from your partner as you swing. It often prevents dizziness to look at your partner as you swing (Fig. 4).

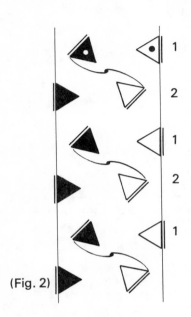

(Fig. 2)

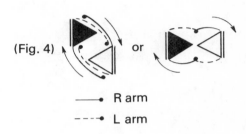

(Fig. 4)   or

⸺⸺• R arm
----• L arm

B All the couple "1's" join **R** hands and walk down the inside of the set (eight counts). Without releasing hands, they turn and walk back up the set to place, separate, go behind their couple "2's", and end in the position below the "2's" (eight counts). As the couple "1's" move into the position below the "2's", the "2's" move slightly up the set. Because of the difference in distance, the steps down the set need to be smaller than those going up the set and around couple "2" (Fig. 3).

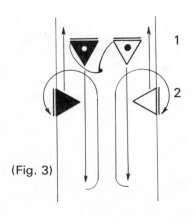

(Fig. 3)

95. The Busy Bass

Recorder or Voices on "ah"

BX *

Teaching Suggestions:

Teach the following rhythm from notation.

1.

Try to discover this rhythm

2.

by omitting all the eighth notes from the first rhythmic pattern given.

Transfer second rhythm to various instruments on which tone clusters can be played. E.g.

Make up different forms.

* Non-chromatic instruments should be set up as follows: C, D, E, F, G, A, B-flat, B, C, D, E, F.

96. Lamento

Develop a suitable instrumentation with the students.

97. Carillon

215

98. Nottamun Town

Southern Appalachians

* with lowered E string

1. In Nottamun town, not a soul would look up,
   Not a soul would look up, not a soul would look down,
   Not a soul would look up, not a soul would look down,
   To show me the way to fair Nottamun town.

2. I rode a gray horse that was called a gray mare,
   With a gray mane and tail, green stripes down her back,
   Gray mane and gray tail, green stripes down her back,
   There wa'ntva hair on her but what was coal black.

3. She stood so still, she threw me to the dirt,
   She tore my hide, and bruised my shirt,
   From saddle to stirrup I mounted again,
   And on my ten toes I rode over the plain.

4. Set down on a hard, hot, cold-frozen stone,
   Ten thousand stood round me, and yet I's alone;
   Took my hat in my hands for to keep my head warm;
   Ten thousand got drownded that never were born.

99. Canon in 5

Suggestions for accompaniments

- Transpose the canon for Soprano recorders to start on a D

- Play Soprano and Alto together

- Add a third voice in the third measure

- Play non-pitched percussion in different meters against the 5 melody

100. Metamorphosis

When wa - ter turns

When ice turns back in - to

water   does   it   re - mem - ber   it   was   ice _____ ?

223

Except for the soprano recorder part and the change of meter/accent (4-3-4), the instrumental parts are not difficult. The setting combines Phrygian and Dorian transposed with A the tonic and using F-sharp and B-flat where needed. The music establishes a mood for movement improvisation. If you do not have an advanced recorder student, play that part yourself, or, since this is material for older children, the recorder part could be played on either flute or oboe.

225

101. Ev'ry Night When the Sun Goes In

Appalachian

in _____ ev' - ry   night _____ when the sun goes   in _____ ev' - ry

227

night _____ when the sun goes in _____ I hang down my head _____ and mourn -ful

230

233

234

235

102. Thus Saith the Lord

237

"Alleluia" may be sung as an alternate text:

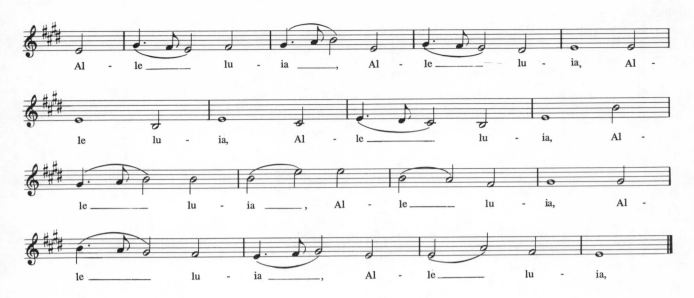

Al - le lu - ia ___, Al - le ___ lu - ia, Al -
le lu - ia, Al - le ___ lu - ia, Al -
le ___ lu - ia ___, Al - le ___ lu - ia, Al -
le ___ lu - ia ___, Al - le ___ lu - ia,

103. The City

V: In the morn - ing the ci - ty spreads its wings, Mak - ing a song in stone that sings.

Tr
Tamb
Cl
HD

V: In the even - ing the ci - ty goes to bed, Hang - ing lights a - bove its head.

SM
AM

❚ is a symbol for a cluster of random pitches. Change pitches each time.

104. From "Song of Exposition"

V 1	Long and long has the grass been growing,
V 2	Long Long
Instruments*	𝄢

V 1	Long and long has the rain been falling,
V 2	Long Long Long
Instruments*	𝄢 𝄢

V 1	Long has the globe been rolling around.
V 2	Long Long Long
Instruments*	𝄢 𝄢

* Find pitched or non-pitched instrumental colors which
support each phrase of text.

105. Two Rhymes to Change Time

1. INSTRUCTIONS

If you should ev-er choose To las-so kang-a-roos, Use one mile of rope And a large dose of hope And main-ly a ver-y tall lad-der.

2. EARLY BIRD

Duple Meter

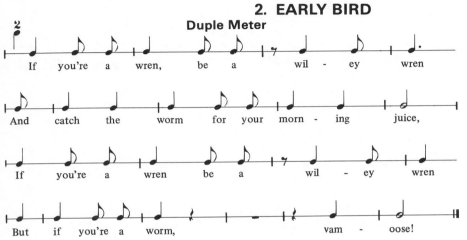

If you're a wren, be a wil-ey wren
And catch the worm for your morn-ing juice,
If you're a wren be a wil-ey wren
But if you're a worm, vam-oose!

Triple Meter

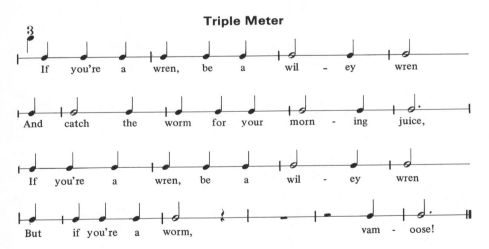

If you're a wren, be a wil-ey wren
And catch the worm for your morn-ing juice,
If you're a wren, be a wil-ey wren
But if you're a worm, vam-oose!

Changing Meter

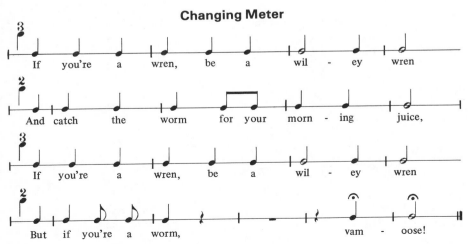

If you're a wren, be a wil-ey wren
And catch the worm for your morn-ing juice,
If you're a wren, be a wil-ey wren
But if you're a worm, vam-oose!

106. Go 'Way from My Window

bo - ther   me - no   more

107. A Flea and a Fly

Version I

Speech: A flea and a fly in a flue, Were caught, so what did they do? Said the

fly "Let us flee", Said the flea, "Let us fly", So they flew through a flaw in the flue. They

flew through a flaw, They flew through a flaw, They flew through a flaw in the flue, They

flew through a flaw, They flew through a flaw, They flew through a flaw in the flue.

* Second entrance of canon

250

Version 2

* Second entrance of canon

NOTE: This speech exercise may also be done in canon by two groups or soloists, without the speech at all and played as a hand drum canon, with the drum held between the knees, or with alternating hands. In the latter case, the claps are played at the rim, and accented slightly.

251

Version 3

NOTE: Use two drums of quite different sizes. The canon begins in the middle of the bar. The drums should be held between the knees.

Version 4

NOTE: The soloist should play with the inflection of his voice, and Group I must imitate EXACTLY. It should come out quite differently each time there's a new soloist, with variations in tempo and dynamics as well as inflection and timbre.

In B, Groups 1 and 2 must remember to speak in their own natural ranges, while imitating the soloist's inflection. In A and C Group II sing-songs its ostinato, starting medium high, with each word lower in pitch than the one before, starting again at the original pitch on "Flea" each time.

Version 5

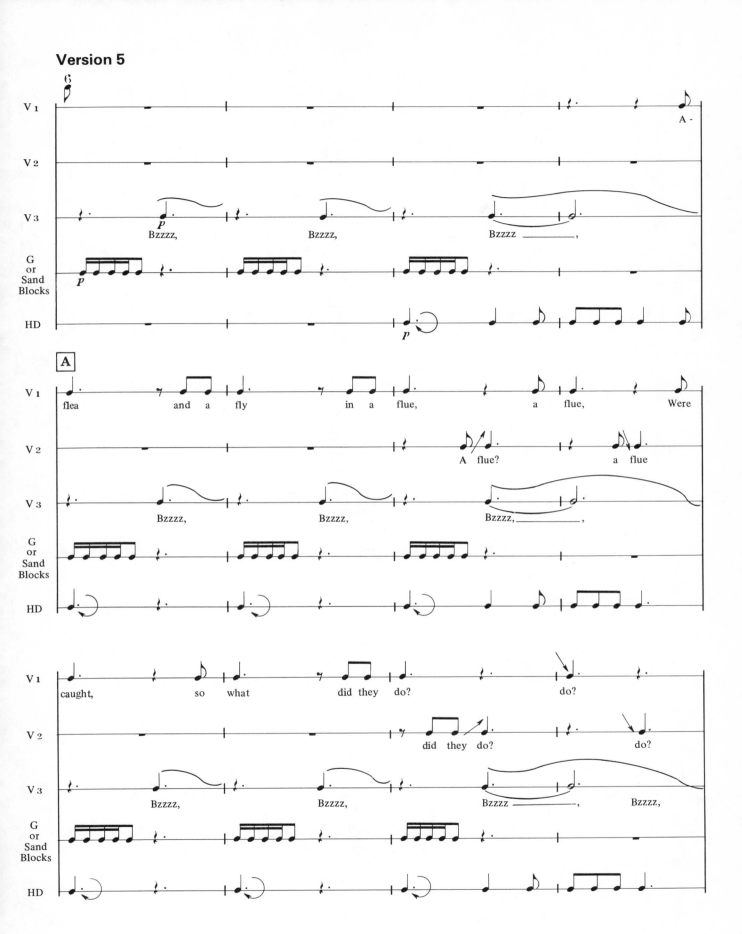

255

NOTE: The wavy lines over the Bzzzz's indicate the inflection suggested. So do the arrows. The ♪ in the Hand Drum part indicates playing with the fingernails on the drum skin, describing a circle on the first half of the bar, with a light touch and a sharp accent at the beginning of the movement.

108. Developing Chord Changes (I-vi-ii-V)

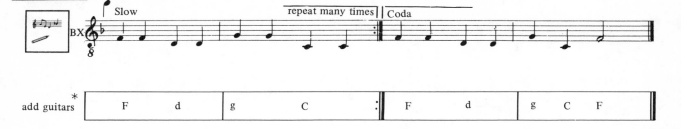

Slow

BX

add guitars *

| F | d | g | C | : | F | d | g | C | F |

or SX
and AX

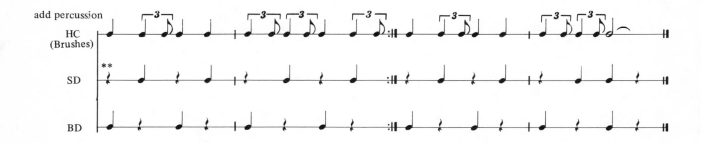

add percussion

HC
(Brushes)

SD **

BD

Now improvise melodies • Singing
               • playing on glockenspiels, recorders

using the whole scale

Change tonality and meter, e.g.

Soprano and
Alto instruments,

Bass instruments.

  *   Capital letters major chords, small letters minor
     chords.
** Strike the rim of the drum while holding the tip of
     the drum stick on the skin (rim shot).

109. Old Blue

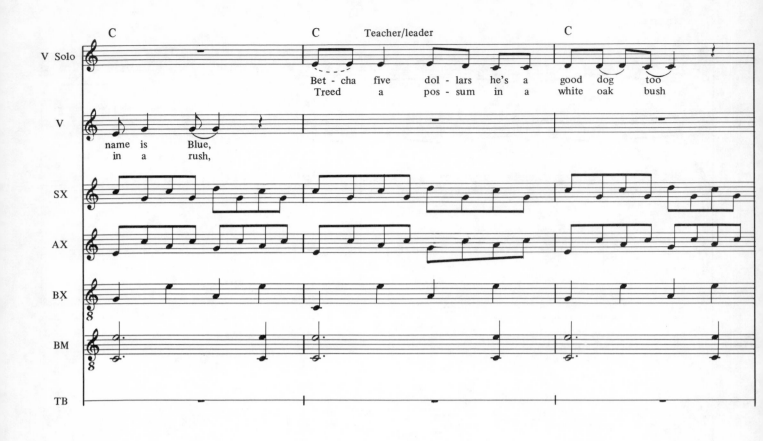

261

262

3. Old Blue died and he died so hard
   Shook up the holes in my backyard.
4. When I get to heaven, first thing I'll do,
   Take up my horn and I'll blow for Blue.

263

110. Scherzo

* Add Alto R

264

** add Si R

265

111. Life is Fine

2. I took the elevator
   Sixteen floors above the ground
   I thought about my baby
   And thought I would jump down

   I stood there and I hollered!
   I stood there and I cried!
   If it hadn't a-been so high
   I might've jumped and died.
       But it was
       High up there!
       It was high!

3. So since I'm still here livin'
   I guess I will live on
   I could've died for love—
   But for livin' I was born.

   Though you may hear me holler,
   And you may see me cry—
   I'll be dogged, sweet baby,
   If you gonna see me die.
       Life is fine!
       Fine as wine!
       Life is fine!

267

112. The Fairy Tale of Teeny-Flea and Weeny-Louse

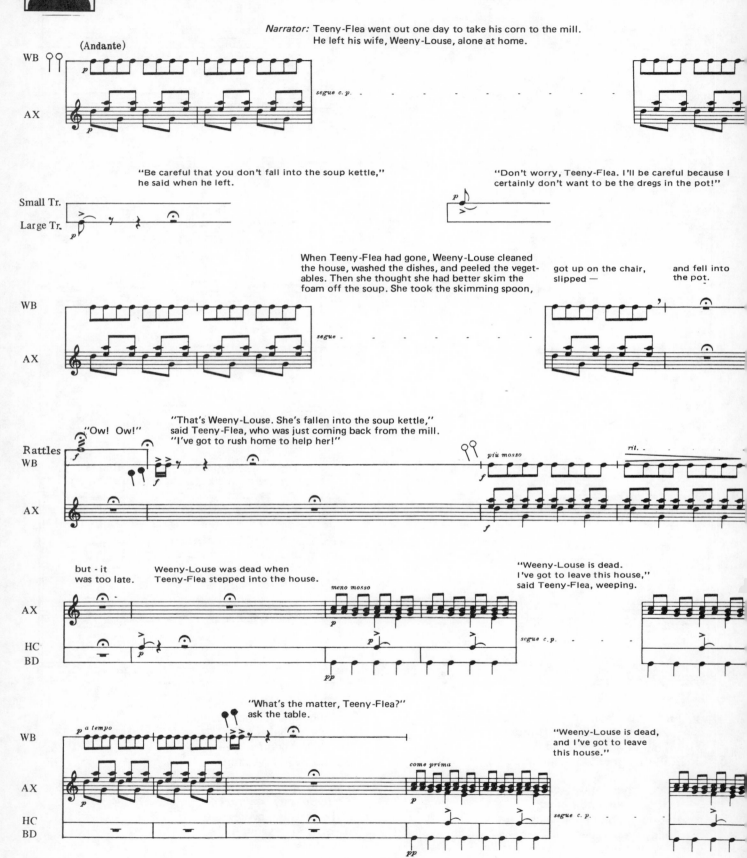

"And I, — I will untable myself and follow you."

The table and Teeny-Flea went past the mixing bowl.

"What's the matter, Teeny-Flea, that you're weeping so?" asked the bowl.

"Weeny-Louse is dead, I've got to leave this house, and my companion has untabled himself."

"And I, — I will unbowl myself and follow you!"

Then they went past the door. "Where are you going?" asked the door.

"Weeny-Louse is dead, I'm leaving the house, the table has untabled himself, and the bowl has unbowled himself."

"And I, — I will unhinge myself!"

A tree stood nearby.

"Where are you going, Teeny-Flea?"

"Weeny-Louse is dead, I've got to leave this house, the table has untabled himself, the bowl has unbowled himself, and the door has unhinged himself."

"And I, — I will uproot myself."

Teeny-Flea, the table, the bowl, the door, and the tree went along until they came to an old woman who was filling her pitchers with water from the well.

"Where are you going, Teeny-Flea?"

269

"Weeny-Louse is dead, I've got to leave this house,
the table has untabled himself, the bowl has unbowled
himself, the door has unhinged himself, and the tree
has uprooted himself."

"Since Weeny-Louse is dead,
I will break both my pitchers,

and follow you."

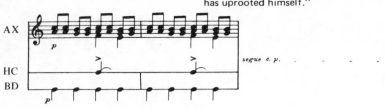

The woman broke both pitchers, and Teeny-Flea, the table, the door, the tree, and the old woman went away and never came back.

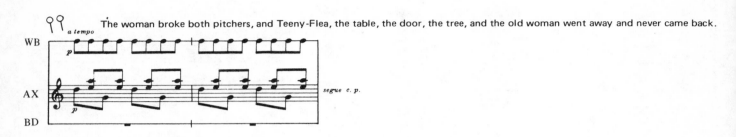

The Brothers Grimm: Translation, Patricia Brown

MUSIK FÜR KINDER, Vol. V

270

113. Entrad, Pastores, Entrad

Puerto Rico

En - trad   pas - to - res   en -
Come in   shep - herds, please   come

trad   En - trad za - ga - las   tam - bien,   En, el por - tal de Be - lén   al
in,   come in herds - men, you come too,   through the gate   of Beth - le - hem,   to a-

solo or small group:

rar ___. Yo be - so tu ma - ni - to, y tu pie in - fan - til,
vine ___. Now I kiss your ti - ny hand, and your ba - by foot,

Duet or two small groups

Tu bo - ca pe - que - ñi - ta y tu pecho in - fan - til ___. E - res luz de mis
Now I kiss __ your ti - ny mouth and your soft ba - by skin __. You ___ are the

Spanish Pronunciation:
A = "Ah"
E = "Eh"
E between two consonants = "Ay"
I = "Ee"
O = "Oh"
U = "Oo"
Y = "Ee"

Consonants as in English except
Ñ = "Ny"
Z = "S"
R = "Rrrr" (Flipped R)
QU = "K"

ELLISIONS occur in singing where the rhythm requires it. e.g.
Mi amor = MeeAmór, with the first syllable pronounced very quickly, almost like a grace note.
NOTE: Although a singable English translation is provided, it is hoped that this carol will be sung in Spanish, since the style is so essentially Spanish, and the pronunciation presents no particular hazards.

114. Two Villançicos from Puerto Rico

Felices Pascuas, Señores

Vamos Pastorcitos

* HD held between the knees. All accents are played
with the thumb on HD; on the larger drum if bongos
are used. The drum part is traditional.

115. More Compositions

A. Warm-up — "What is it like?" —
1. to be an ice cube melting?
2. to walk through melted marshmellows?
3. to walk on pinheads?
4. to squeeze through the eye of a needle?
5. to be hurled into outer space? etc.
   The class responds with movement to these and other suggestions.

B. Abstract design in motion
   (These exercises demand co-operation and the ability to focus on problem solving. Simplicity and clarity are the key words in experimentation. They also demand familiarity, flexibility, imagination and sophistication in the use of movement vocabulary.)

1. Small groups select no more than four of the designs below.

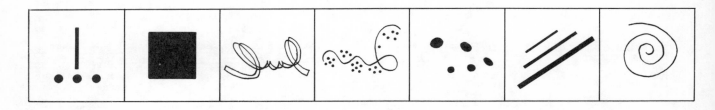

2. These designs provide a score from which to read. Each group decides on its final piece.
   a. A form for the piece is chosen; ABA, rondo, ABCD, canon, etc.
   b. Movement explorations are made; the process of working it out is more valuable and will accomplish the task more readily than a lot of talk.
   c. The movement may be accompanied by vocal sounds and/or integrated use of instruments; e.g. if the last design is chosen, the group could get in a circle and begin to turn clockwise, getting faster and faster, with joined hands being raised, a low to high vocal sound being added until the group reaches a stopping point.

3. Each group, after experimenting and completing its movement piece, presents it to the class.

C. Poetry in motion
1. In small groups, each group is given the following skeleton of a poem to complete, as the teacher carefully reads and explains how to complete it.

   > (Color) is like a (noun metaphor)
   >   it (action verb, implying movement)
   >   and (another verb)
   >   and (another verb)
   > (same color) is a (noun)
   > (same color) is a (noun)
   >   It is like a (same metaphor as above)

2. Once the groups complete the poem in their own way, with their own chosen color and nouns and verbs, they experiment with moving to it, how to say it; they decide on voice or instrument accompaniments, etc., the teacher serves only as a guide when necessary.

3. Each group performs its poem for the rest of the class.
   Example of completed poem:

   > Orange is like a flame
   >   it leaps
   >   and flies
   >   and flutters
   > Orange is a sun
   > Orange is a star
   > It is like a flame

116. Turtledove

Appalachian

1. Fare you well, my dear, I must be — gone, and — leave you for a — while. If I go a - way, I'll come back a - gain, tho' I roam ten thou-sand

281

I will do for thee, my love, as ___ I will do for thee.

117. Allegro in Lydian Mode

118. The Ins and Outs of Texture

Round up the following for your class:

FOOD: jello — toll house cookies — a juice

MUSIC: B. Britten's "Young Person's Guide to the Orchestra"

Early Music: Medieval Vol I., (or something comparably thin in texture from that period)

ART: A contemporary print such as a Jackson Pollack, A Mondrian.

TODAY: A contemporary living room with multi-textured décor.... an Andrew Wyeth interior .... a Shaker living room .... A Baroque drawing room or castle interior.

FABRIC: Satin tweed, canvas, silk, burlap, velvet, sandpaper

MISC: Buttons in a box, etc.

POETRY: Lewis Carroll, "Jabberwocky" — Langston Hughes, "Dream Dust"

As a teacher, invent ways of comparing and contrasting the textures in these areas. Find ways of setting the two above poems utilizing the moods created by the thick and thinness of textures. Write with the class a thickly textured percussion piece on a large piece of craft paper for all to see. Listen to the Britten recording and have the children draw their impressions at the end of the fugue where all the instruments are in a tangle. Compare these impressions with the Jackson Pollack print. Have students close their eyes and experience by feel the various fabric textures. See if they can create a movement to go with what they have just felt....Have other children try to guess which texture they are depicting in movement.

119. Dream Dust

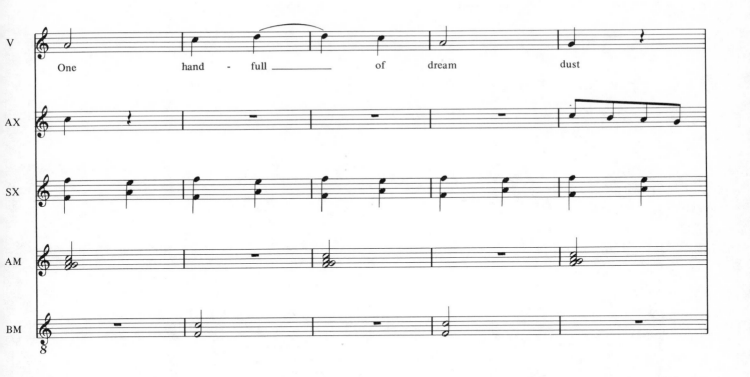

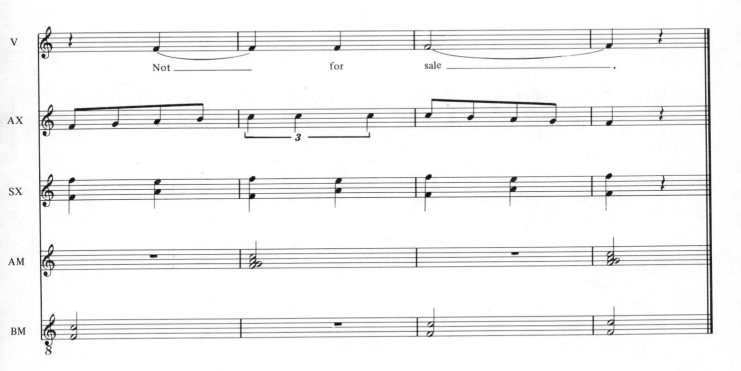

In this piece the AX has been placed above the SX in the score to show the interaction between the vocal line and that of the alto xylophone.

* The AX line can also be played on the soprano recorder.

120. Rhythmic Exercise

Start slowly with this exercise and gradually increase the tempo to MM. ♪ = 240

A is the basic rhythm. It can be clapped, vocalized, or used with a text.

B has the rhythmic line played by one instrument and accompanied with the main accents on another.

C is the rhythm orchestrated for sound gestures.

D is a transference of C to non-pitched percussion.

121. St. Ives

not too fast

V: As I was go - ing to St. Ives I met a man with

se - ven wives.

1. Eve - ry wife had se - ven sacks.
2. Eve - ry sack had se - ven cats. Kits, cats,
3. Eve - ry cat had se - ven kits.

289

*Wood blocks, hand drums, or any combination of untuned percussion.

122. Mixolydian Dance

* Open G tuning for guitar, lower pitch as follows:

E A D G B E
↓ ↓   ↓   strum across all strings
D G   D

Alternately: capo on 3rd fret, play E position chord.

After piece has been played often, players should be able to make a dance that emphasizes the contrasting melodies; group vs. solo; lines/circles; circle/partners. One possibility is shown below:

Circle of dancers with bells on ankles: facing counter-clockwise hands joined, low, or hanging free.

A section

Step R hop | L hop | R L | R hop | L hop | R hop | L R | L close

B section Arms low and to right knees bent, standing still, arms describe an arc overhead ending on left side (4 bars) in remaining 4 bars, return same way to place, knees straighten as arms pass overhead. Head follows arms (this movement can be adjusted so that dancers end facing clockwise to repeat the dance).

123. Sellenger's Round

Bowed String Instruments may also be used for this instrumentation.
Alto and tenor parts altered, length of piece altered to fit the dance form.

Sellenger's Round (or, The Beginning of the World)

This is a very old round dance for couples, though the steps are the same for each person. Several patterns basic to traditional English dancing appear in it.

[A] With hands joined, the dancers do eight slipping steps (side-gallops), clockwise,

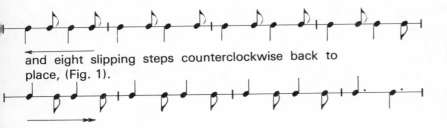

and eight slipping steps counterclockwise back to place, (Fig. 1).

(Fig. 1)

Facing partner, each person "sets" to his own R (small, light "single" done sideways as R, L, R) and then L (L, R, L). (Fig. 2).

(Fig. 2)

[CHORUS]

Moving to the center, "single" R and "single" L. (A single is step-close-step; in this sequence, it would be R-L-R, L-R-L.)

Moving back to place, a "double" (four steps R, L, R, L).

ending with a "turn single" in place (four steps to own R),

This whole sequence is repeated.

B With hands joined, forward a "double" (R, L, R, L) and back to place with a "double" (R, L, R, L). This is done two times. **B** is very similar to the chorus and must not be confused with it.

CHORUS

C "Siding:" partners change places passing L shoulders (R, L, R) and make half-turn as feet are closed on fourth count; they return to places passing R shoulders (L, R, L) and another half-turn. The full siding sequence is done twice (Fig. 3).

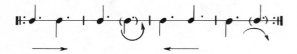

(Fig. 3)

CHORUS

D "Arming:" partners link R arms, make a complete turn clockwise, separate, and "fall back" to place. This is repeated linking L arms and turning counterclockwise. There are eight steps for each turn.

CHORUS

A is repeated

FINAL CHORUS

usually ends with a bow to partner.

124. Lollipop

To be used early in a unit directed toward new forms in music and poetry. <u>The poem is the musical score.</u> Please see eyes, nose and mouth in bold print.

Suggestions for Development:

Use the five syllabic sounds in the poem: lol li pop ove lick (the plural —pops— may be treated with dynamics; allow children freedom to explore and invent).

— Select a nonsense mouth sound for each syllable.
— Divide class and assign one mouth sound to each group.
— Each group responds with appropriate mouth sound when the syllable occurs in the poem.
— Record on tape recorder at slow speed; play back at fast speed, or vice versa. Poem may be repeated several times for fast play back.
— Change from mouth sounds and assign unpitched instruments to each syllabic sound. Tape as before.
— Change from unpitched instruments to pitched sounds. Use dissonant intervals such as minor seconds, tone clusters, etc. Tape as before.
— Select one section of the tape as section A, another for B and still another for C, then create a rondo.
— Decide upon a time value for each syllable and create still another composition. Try augmentation and diminution. Try one against the other.
— Execute in retrograde.
— Create a composition with both the forward and retrograde "melody" simultaneously.
— Create a canon with each of the above and then execute as a double canon.

lolli

lolli pop

pop lolli pop

lolli pop lolli

lolli pop lolli pop

lolli **pop** *pop* **pop** *lolli*

love lickin a lolli pop

pops love lickin lolli pops

*pick a l***oll***i of a pop*

*love l***o***lli love pop*

lick a **lolli** *pop love*

love love love love

pop **lolli** *pop*

lolli pop

lolli

p

p

p

p

p

p

o

p

p

p

p

p

125. Loneliness

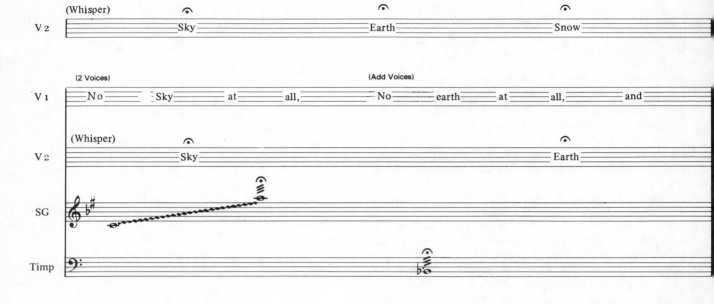

"Loneliness" from AN INTRODUCTION TO HAIKU, copyright © 1958 by Harold G. Henderson. Reprinted by permission of Doubleday and Company, Inc.

126. Making a "Tone Row" Piece

- Provide chromatic bars for all instruments.
- Mix them up — select 8 to put back in random order. (The more mixed up the better!)
- Listen to the resulting rows from each instrument.
- Choose a row that sounds interesting and set up all instruments this way. This is a time consuming procedure, more suited to a small group than to a 30-pupil class. In a larger class not all students would have a chance to play their rows.
- Explain to the class that this row of tones is going to be the basis for a piece the group is going to compose.
- The class then decides if they wish to play the row in any specific rhythm as an opening statement.
- Consider various ways of playing the row
  — different tempi
  — different timbres
  — using only fragments
  — playing in augmentation, diminution
  — playing against itself
  — playing in retrograde

What the students produce, of course, depends on the background of the class and what kind of classroom music experiences they have had.

If the experiences are extensive, the lists of material will be also and the teacher will have to use considerable skill in helping the students organize it. If the students have had limited experience, the teacher can suggest several new techniques without overloading the class.

- Discuss possibilities for accompaniments
  — tremolo
  — tone clusters
  — ametric uses of non-pitched percussion

After the vocabulary has been gathered, a form is necessary.
- Decide together whether the form will be a traditional one, like a rondo, through-composed, or some other logically constructed form.

- Decide if graphic notation is necessary to remember the piece.
- Practice and perform the piece.

For students with experience and background, the class can be divided into groups of 4 or 5 students each to make their pieces by the same procedure. This method will take longer than the first. Each group might share its piece with the others. Comparing and discussing should be encouraged.

Group pieces can be made after the whole class makes one. When the activity is over, explain to the class that "professional" composers have also written pieces using tone rows, generally made up of the 12 chromatic tones, but using the same technique which they used.

Here is an example from "The Moon Rises," a composition by Ernst Křenek (part of Twelve Short Piano Pieces, published by G. Schirmer).

The tone row can be played on the piano by the teacher. (Live music makes analysis more immediate and meaningful to the children).

This tone row includes several intervals of thirds. Křenek often produces chords which in a different context could easily be analysed in the traditional manner.

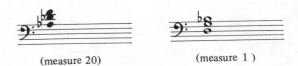

(measure 20)   (measure 1)

127. Schönberg Study

This piece demonstrates the use of repeated minor thirds. It should be played as an introduction to the piece after which it is modelled: Arnold Schönberg, Six Little Pieces for Piano, opus 19, No. 2.

Similarities and differences of both pieces should be pointed out to the children. One possibility for teaching the xylophone part is to substitute a dot (•) for each note and a slanted line (/) for each rest. This creates a sort of visual "Morse Code" making the form easier to understand and learn.

Recording : Piano Music of Berg, Schönberg and Webern
Beveridge Webster, piano
Dover records HCR-5285
(side 1, band 3, piece 2)

128. Poem

As the cat
climbed over
the top of

the jamcloset
first the right
forefoot

carefully
then the hind
stepped down

into the pit of
the empty
flowerpot.

129. The Tickle Rhyme

"Who's that tickling my back?" said the wall.
"Me," said a small
Caterpillar. "I'm learning
To crawl."

130. Our Washing Machine
by Patricia Hubbell

Our washing machine went whisity whirr
Whisity whisity whisity whirr
One day at noon it went whisity click
Whisity whisity whisity click
Click grr click grr click grr click
Call the repairman
Fix it . . . Quick!

Suggestions:

— In place of nonsense words create instead:
   mouth sounds in rhythmic pattern
   unpitched instrumental sounds in rhythmic pattern
   movement, both locomotor and non-locomotor, to
      suggest each of the nonsense sounds.

— Dramatize
   combine the above in many ways.
   use as ostinato and/or introduction, and/or inter-
      ludes etc. Expand by adding more nonsense
      sounds.
   try accelerando, ritardando, crescendo, decres-
      cendo, especially the last two lines.

— as culmination, create accompaniment with pitched
   percussion instruments.

131. I am a Bird

Lyrics in vocal line:
I am a black - bird with a bright red beak fly - ing
in - to the pit of the sky _____.

*Strike cymbal with the stick end of the mallet

132. Kulu #2

Percussion Instrumentation

2 hanging cymbals 1 pair bongos 1 or 2 congas or 1 deep drum (with soft mallets)

— 1 pair claves 𝅘𝅥𝅮𝅘𝅥𝅮 , 𝅘𝅥𝅮𝅘𝅥𝅮𝅘𝅥𝅮 , 𝅘𝅥𝅮𝅘𝅥𝅮 ♪ 𝅘𝅥𝅮𝅘𝅥𝅮𝅘𝅥𝅮𝅘𝅥𝅮 or other 16th note patterns
— 1 pair maracas ⌀⌀⌀ shaken slowly in a circle (as music intensifies, maracas should be shaken, more quickly)
— 1 cowbell or cowbell-like instrument 𝅘𝅥𝅮𝅘𝅥𝅮𝅘𝅥𝅮

— 1 set temple blocks played with wrapped mallets (only the lowest two blocks used.)
— Percussion should be played at beginning as written; elsewhere exact entrances are up to conductor within general guidelines indicated.

* it available, alto saxophones at pitch

302

This piece introduces some techniques that are a part of contemporary Black Music: a vocal line built with motives that make it almost instrumental, percussion parts freely performed which provide an underlying sound carpet, and gradual intensification of all parts to a climactic end. Tension should be maintained throughout the piece even when sounds are widely separated as in the beginning. The vocal part may be doubled by recorder until pitches are learned. It would be better not to use recorders in performance but rather alto saxophones which have a more characteristic sound. Of course, if saxophones are unavailable, use recorders.

 "Kulu 2" serves as an introduction to "Kulu Se Mama" written by Julian Lewis and performed by John Coltrane (The Best of John Coltrane, Impulse ABC Records, stereo AS-9200-2, side 4 band 1.) Note that the opening four note motive of the saxophones on the recording is identical with that of the recorders in "Kulu 2".

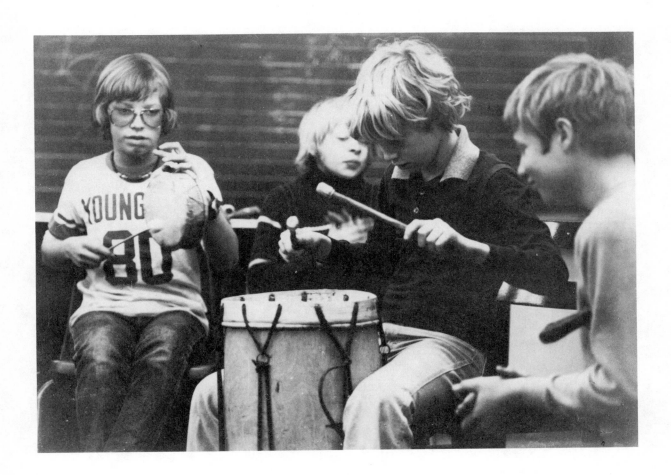

133. Todas Las Tardes

Translation: Every night in Granada, a child dies.

The piece calls for three drinking glasses filled with water to produce pitches a semi-tone or less apart when rubbed around the rim. The glasses should be of good quality and kept moist around the rim or else they will not sound! Recommended pitches are G, G sharp, and A. The castanet part should imitate the written part as closely as possible. The voice part may be doubled by recorder to help ensure pitch accuracy but should not be used in performance.

This piece uses the same text as part IV of George Crumb's ANCIENT VOICES OF CHILDREN and can serve as an introduction to that work.

Recording: George Crumb: ANCIENT VOICE OF CHIL-
DREN
Nonesuch H-71255, side 2, band 1, second
part.

134. The Seafarer

Key and Notes

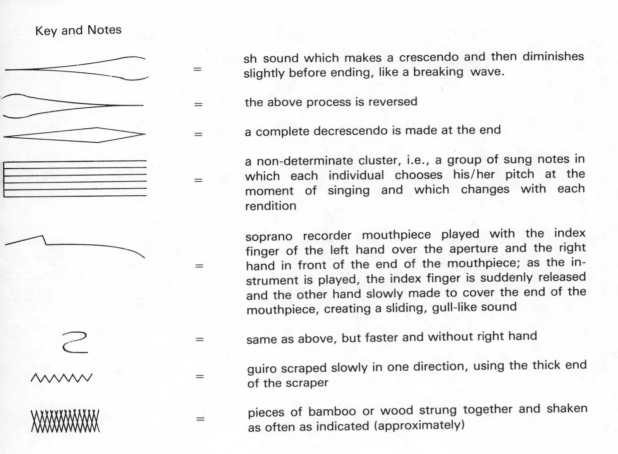

	=	sh sound which makes a crescendo and then diminishes slightly before ending, like a breaking wave.
	=	the above process is reversed
	=	a complete decrescendo is made at the end
	=	a non-determinate cluster, i.e., a group of sung notes in which each individual chooses his/her pitch at the moment of singing and which changes with each rendition
	=	soprano recorder mouthpiece played with the index finger of the left hand over the aperture and the right hand in front of the end of the mouthpiece; as the instrument is played, the index finger is suddenly released and the other hand slowly made to cover the end of the mouthpiece, creating a sliding, gull-like sound
	=	same as above, but faster and without right hand
	=	guiro scraped slowly in one direction, using the thick end of the scraper
	=	pieces of bamboo or wood strung together and shaken as often as indicated (approximately)

All entrances in the introduction, Sections II, IV, and V, should be made when and as indicated in relation to the words. In Sections I and III, only those entrances enclosed in a rectangle (e.g. ▭) must be played as indicated; all others are given only to indicate the general idea and may be filled in as the conductor sees fit. Special care must be taken in Sections II and IV to see that the voice, soprano metallophone and bass metallophone correspond as indicated in the score. Also, in the introduction and Section V, adequate space (1-4 seconds) should be allowed between "waves" to sound like waves on a shore, unless two "waves" overlap in the score. Any overlapping entrances in the introduction of Section V should be performed with the chorus in two groups, one for each part. The text for this piece comes from an old Saxon poem. All the imitative sounds should be as close to the real thing as possible (i.e. the vocal wave sound and recorder-bird sounds). The reader or speaker must be dramatically (but not melodramatically!) gifted. His part must be synchronized closely with instrumental parts in Sections II, III (boxed entrance), IV, and more generally in other sections.

From THE EARLIEST ENGLISH POEMS, translated by Michael Alexander (Penguin Classics, 1966) © Michael Alexander, 1966.

Introduction

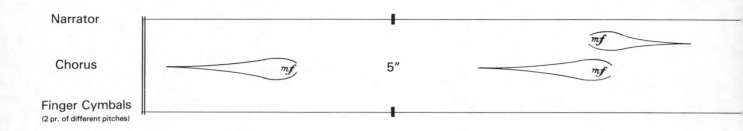

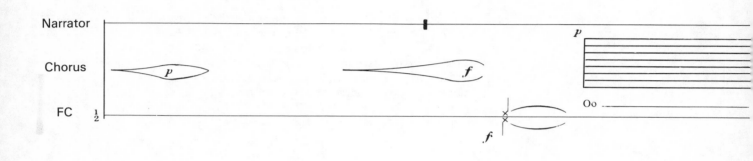

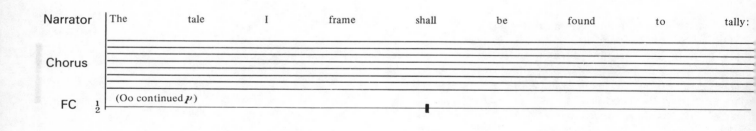

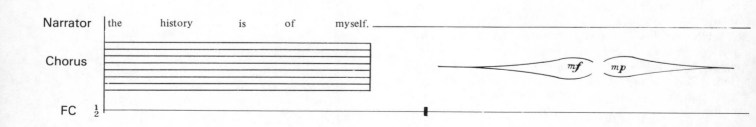

I

Narrator: Sitting day-long at

2 small (HC)
2 large
1 medium tam-tam (gong)
Played near edge

Narrator: an oar's end clenched against clinging sorrow, breast-drought

HC
Tam-tam

Narrator: have I borne, and bitternesses too. I have coursed my keel

HC
Tam-tam

Narrator: through care-halls without end over furled foam, I forward

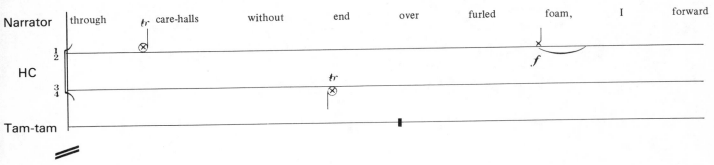

HC
Tam-tam

Narrator: in the bows through the narrowing night, numb, watching for

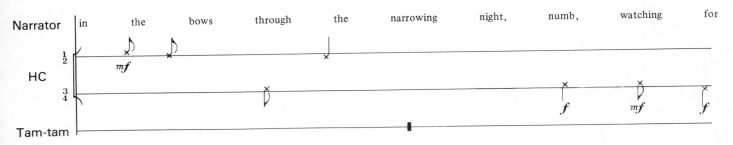

HC
Tam-tam

307

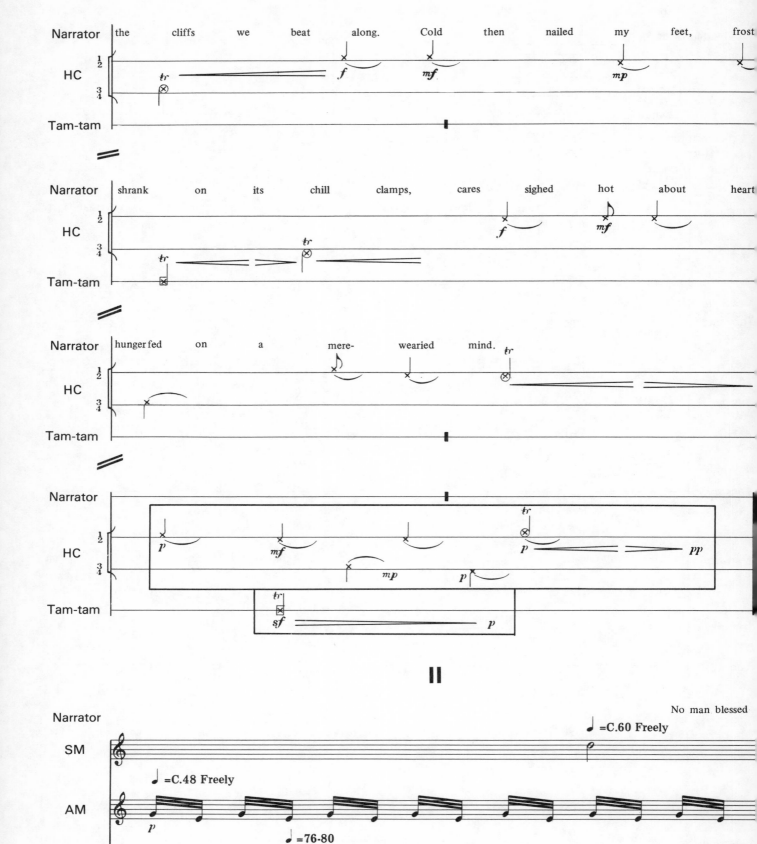

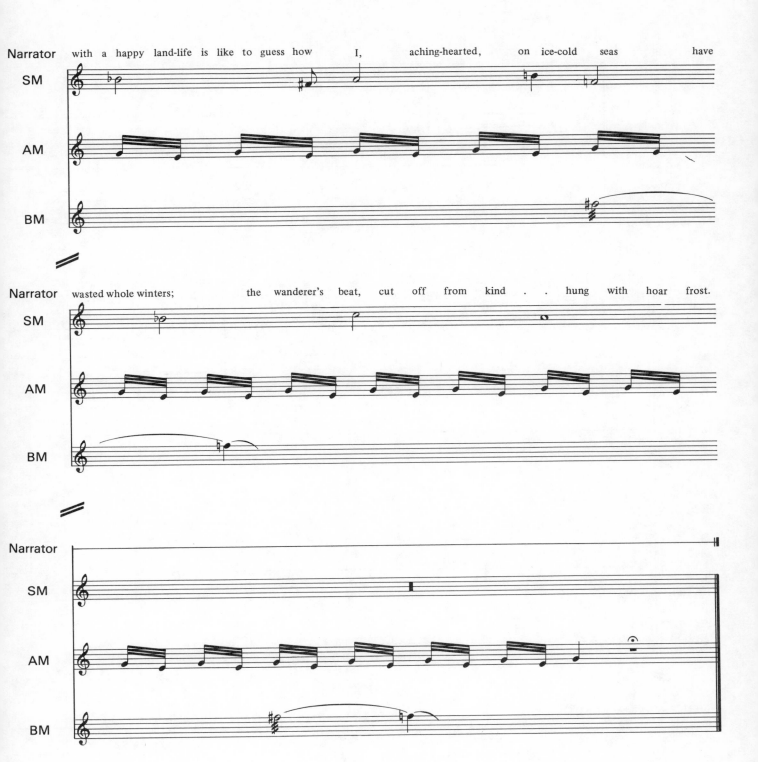

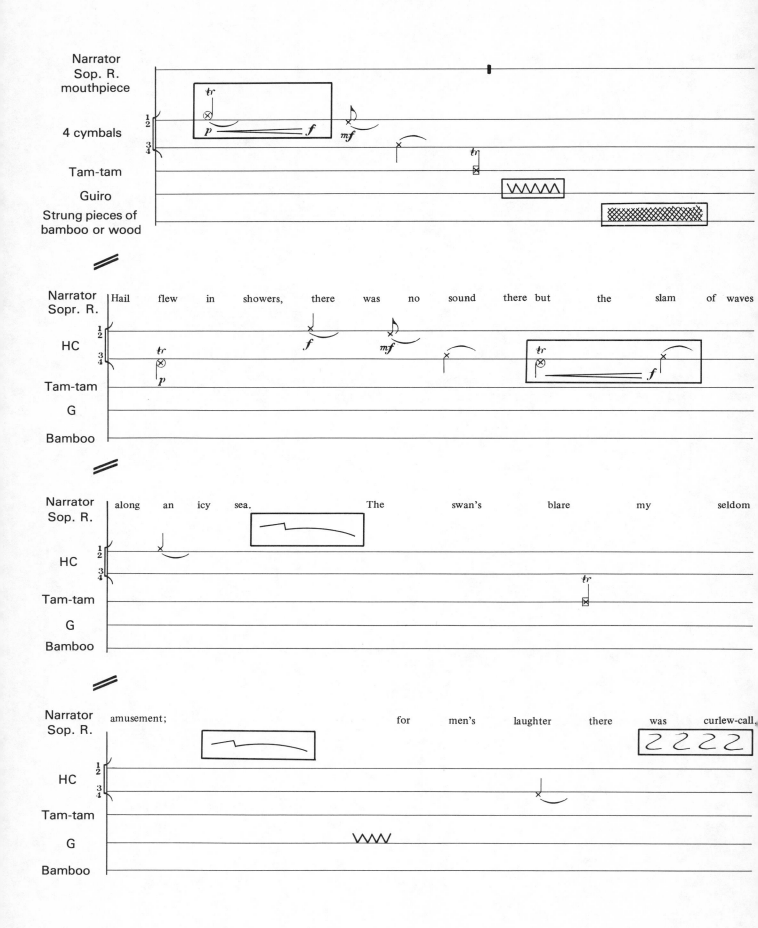

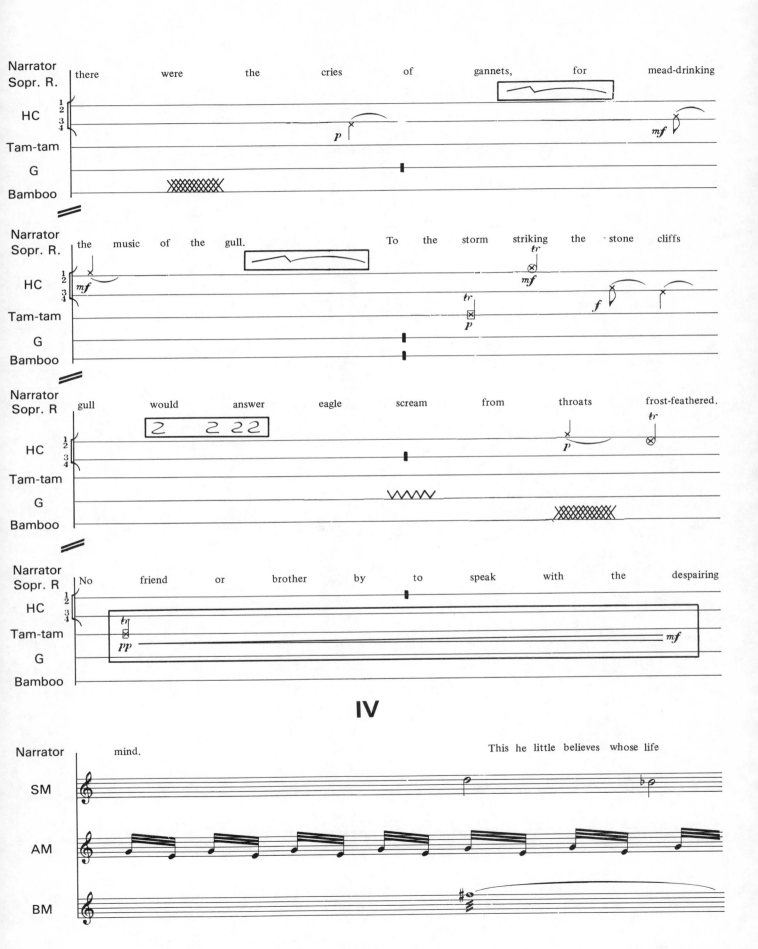

IV

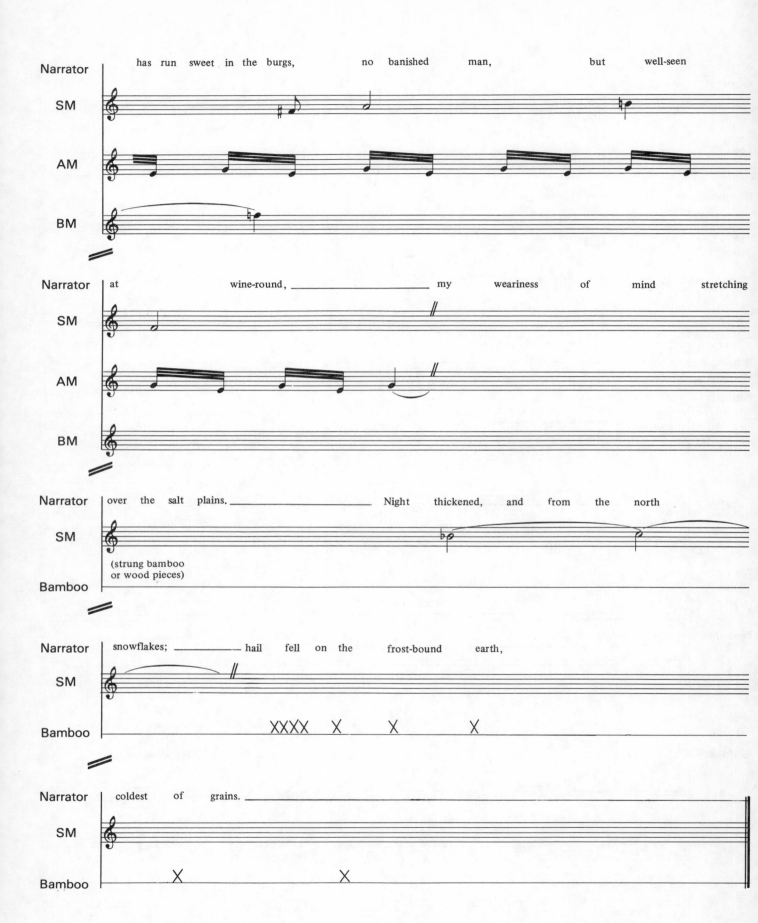

V

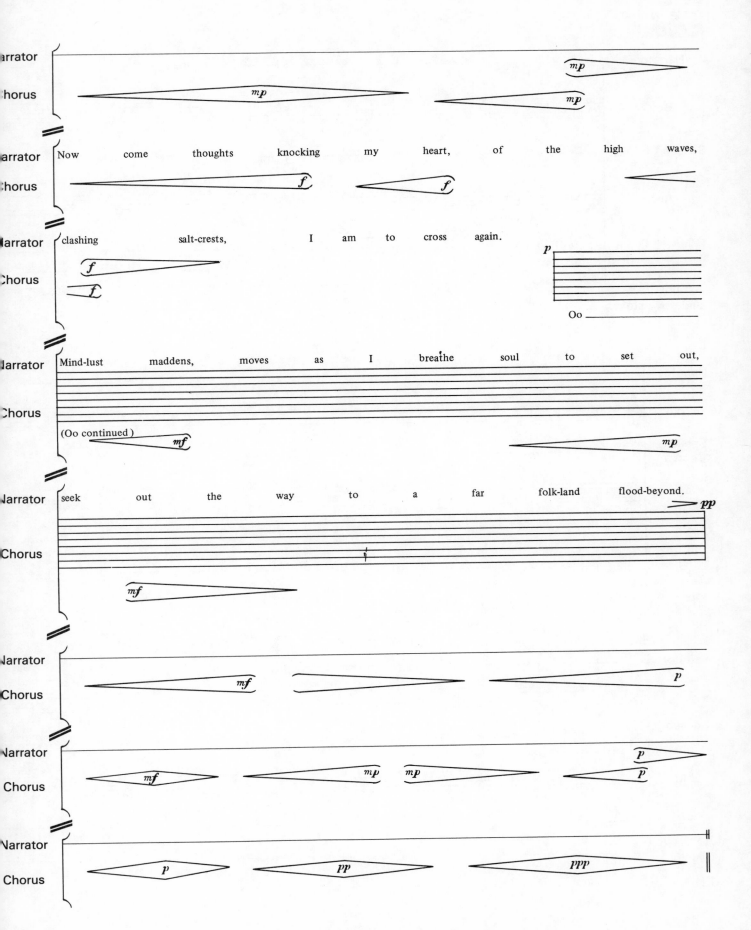

Now come thoughts knocking my heart, of the high waves,

clashing salt-crests, I am to cross again.

Oo

Mind-lust maddens, moves as I breathe soul to set out,

(Oo continued)

seek out the way to a far folk-land flood-beyond.

135. The Little Mute Boy

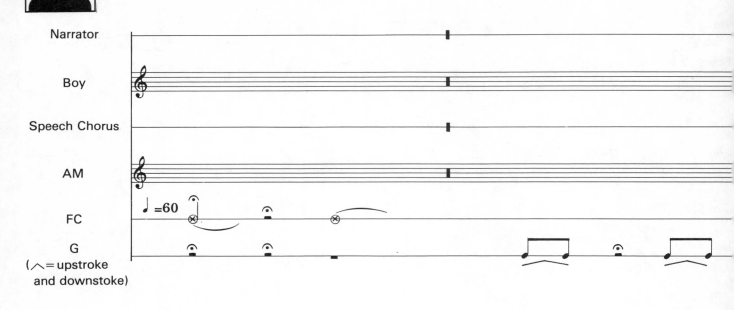

Narrator

Boy

Speech Chorus

AM

FC

G

(⌒ = upstroke
and downstoke)

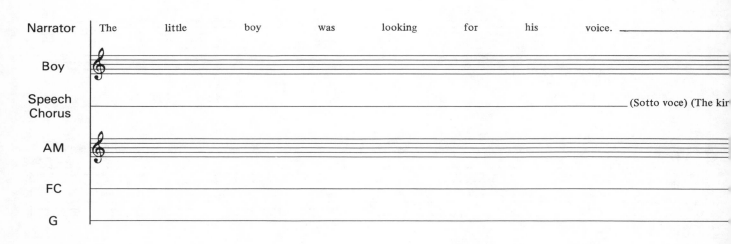

Narrator: The little boy was looking for his voice. _____

Speech Chorus: _____ (Sotto voce) (The kir

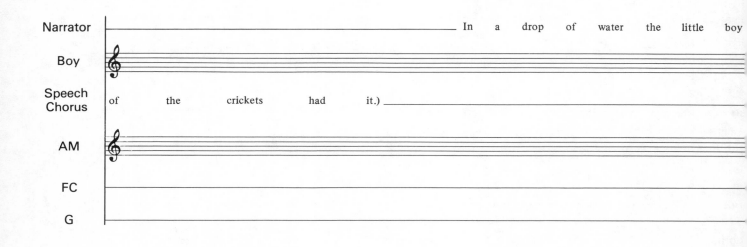

Narrator: _____ In a drop of water the little boy

Speech Chorus: of the crickets had it.) _____

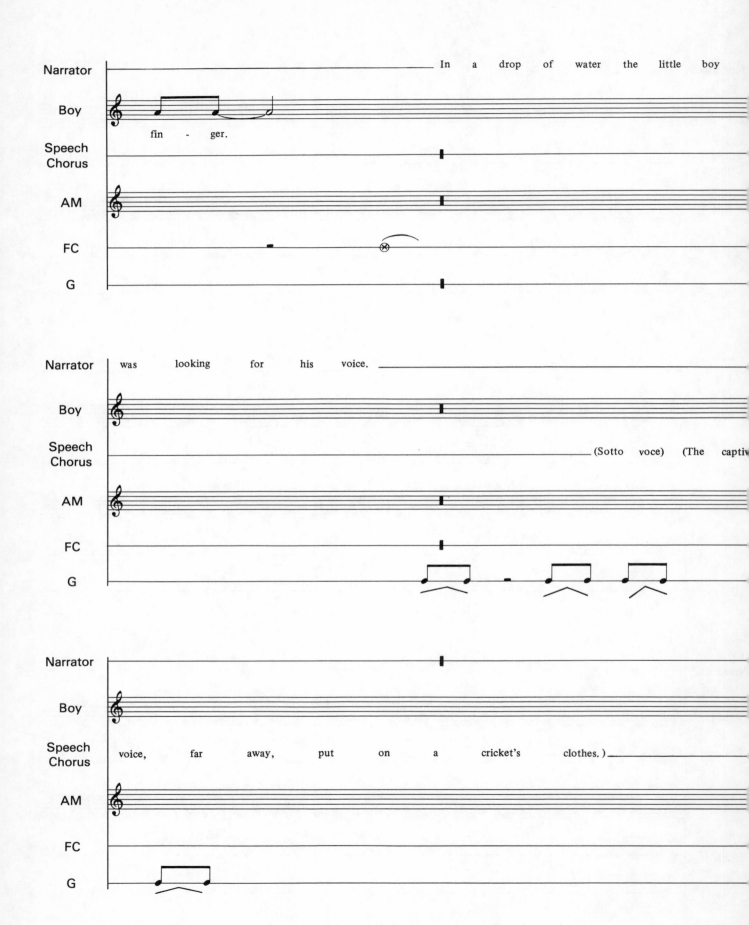

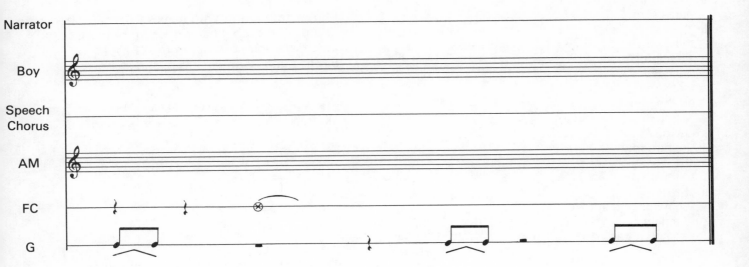

 This piece may be learned along with listening to "Ancient Voices of Children" by George Crumb. (Nonesuch H-71255, side 1, band 1) The texts of both pieces are the same. Learn "The Little Mute Boy" before listening to "Ancient Voices of Children".

136. Poems

In the night,
  oppossum;
In the night,
  the owl;
In the night,
  the bat —
And coyote
  on the prowl.

In the day
  the butterfly;
In the day,
  the bee;
In the day,
  the hummingbird —
And a deer
  beneath a tree.

Reprinted by permission of James Steel Smith.

Weather Words
I know four words with names like some strange tune
Chinook, sirocco, khamsin, and monsoon.
Like water over pebbles in Lost Brook:
Sirocco, monsoon, khamsin, and chinook.

From THE BEAUTIFUL NECESSITY by Claude Bragdon. Reprinted by permission of Alfred A. Knopf, Inc., New York.

The point, the line, the surface and sphere,
In seed, stem, leaf, and fruit appear.

From THE OLD BATEAU AND OTHER POEMS by David McCord. Copyright 1953 by David McCord. By permission of Little, Brown and Company.

Articles

		Page
Patricia Brown	THE ORFF INSTRUMENTARIUM: WHAT IS ITS PURPOSE?	320
Isabel Carley	ABOUT IMPROVISATION	322
Tossi Aaron	PERFORMING: PRO AND CON	326
Jane Frazee	LISTENING: A PARTICIPATORY APPROACH	327
Mary Stringham-Shamrock	ORFF—SCHULWERK AND WORLD MUSICS SOME CONSIDERATIONS	331
Miriam Samuelson	ABOUT DANCE NOTATION	332

The Orff-Instrumentarium: What is its Purpose?

Patricia Brown

This article is a consideration of four points: the function of the Orff instruments as a basic value to the child; their foundation for continuing instrumental study; ways to use, or avoid using, combinations of Orff instruments and other instruments; and the role of the Orff instruments in facilitating further instrumental study.

In his speech at the opening of the Orff Institute on October 25, 1963, Carl Orff said:

"I encouraged the active participation of the students by the playing of their own music, that is through improvising and composing it themselves. I therefore did not want to train them on highly developed art instruments, but rather on instruments that were preferably rhythmic, comparatively easy to learn, primitive, and unsophisticated. Therefore to start with, pitched percussion instruments with wooden and metal bars, such as different kinds of xylophones, metallophones and glockenspiels, were made. The newly constructed xylophones had nothing to do with the orchestral type of xylophone but were based on the highly developed Indonesian models. Without melodic instruments and those capable of sustaining a drone bass, it would have been impossible to develop an independent instrumental ensemble. After some experiments with various exotic types of flute, I decided to use the recorder. For bass instruments, in addition to timpani and the lower barred instruments, we used string instruments such as cellos and violas da gamba to provide a sustained drone bass. Guitars and lutes were also used as plucked strings."

The present-day instrumentarium includes soprano, alto and bass xylophones and metallophones, soprano and alto glockenspiels, various pitched drums such as timpani, bongos, congas, and different sizes of hand drums, and a great variety of non-pitched percussion such as bass drum, snare drum, wood block, temple blocks, cymbal, triangle, sleigh bells, tambourine, maracas, claves, castanets, reco-reco and cow bell. Included among the melodic instruments are other historical woodwinds in addition to the recorder and the bass bordun. Of course, many of these instruments are far from primitive and unsophisticated, but they still can lend their voices in an uncomplicated fashion to the ensemble.

WHAT IS THE VALUE OF THE ENSEMBLE TO THE STUDENT?

This instrumentarium offers every child an opportunity to participate according to his own capacity through the preliminary stages of using speech, singing and the playing of sound gestures (snapping, clapping, patsching and stamping), and then through the addition of pitched and non-pitched percussion, and a melodic or a bass instrument. Each child is able to participate as a member of the ensemble and as a soloist, improvising, interpreting, or recreating a composed piece. The combination of speaking or singing while playing can involve coordination of a very high degree: manual and digital control, laterality, eye-hand and gross and fine motor control.

HOW CAN GOOD TEACHING WITH ORFF INSTRUMENTS AFFECT A CHILD'S FURTHER STUDY?

The careful progression of instrumental training — from voice to sound gestures to small percussion to instruments separated from the player (by mallets, bow, beaters, brushes, and sticks) — gives a child confidence in the ability to make music with instruments. His experience and success naturally encourages his interest in other instruments: historical, folk, band or orchestra.

The child has the opportunity to orchestrate pieces, to select the kind of sound and contrasts he wants from the pitched and non-pitched percussion, to decide which melodic instrument to use if one is needed, and to find the best bass instrument to provide the foundation. Specifically, he can work with a variety of sounds, from the crisp wood timbre of the xylophones to the longer resonating radiating quality of the glockenspiels and metallophones; he can choose from the many timbres represented by the other pitched and non-pitched percussion instruments: metal, wood, skin, and rattles. He can use wind and string instruments for sustained sounds. The barred instruments offer a pitch range of nearly four octaves; this range is considerably extended by the bass and large and small percussion instruments.

By participating in the ensemble, the student's musicianship is strengthened by rhythmic and melodic training, an understanding of form, experimenting with contemporary music, and acquaintance with techniques of composition, the use of traditional notation, and experience with graphic notation. The satisfaction of successful ensemble experience furnishes a strong incentive to ongoing music study.

For various reasons, it may not be possible, feasible or even desirable for every child to study a band or orchestra instrument: time pressures, the expense involved, a physical handicap, or the age or size of the child can be obstacles. The Orff ensemble therefore assures a way for every child to have a musical experience since only minimal technical knowledge is required. In light of this, the ensemble also provides a musical outlet for a child during work on technical problems of scales, fingering, articulation, and music theory. On most of the band or orchestra instruments, one can play only a single line and produce basically one timbre, but on the barred instruments, one can play two or more bars at once, and sometimes produce very different timbres. The Orff ensemble offers opportunities for both joining and separating many lines and sounds.

WHAT PROBLEMS ARE PRESENTED IN COMBINING THE ORFF INSTRUMENTS WITH OTHER INSTRUMENTS?

The first problem is the balance of dynamic levels; the second, the pitch discrepancy; the third, the overtones. The Orff instrumentarium generally produces a quieter, chamber sound since the barred instruments are not meant to produce a wide dynamic range. Contemporary brass and woodwind instruments are much louder than their historic counterparts, and therefore must be played with enough breath and embouchure control to support the pitch and not overpower the barred instruments, not an easy task for a novice. The historic winds and strings such as the recorder, krummhorn, sackbut, and viol are naturally softer, and although they do present pitch problems, they provide much better balance. Piano can be used with the barred instruments, but it is advisable to avoid the octaves encompassed by the instrumentarium, using only the outer reaches of the keyboard to avoid the clash of overtones. One must also take care not to overpower the barred instruments.

Orchestrations involving contrasting groups of instruments can be very striking. If attention is paid to the balance problem, examples of possible juxtapositions of groups of instruments might include present day brass and orchestral timpani contrasted with recorder and hand drum; recorder and guitar contrasted with harpsichord and viol; wood blocks and bass xylophone contrasted with glockenspiel, viol and bass drum; glockenspiel, xylophone and timpani contrasted with xylophone, sleigh bells and hand drum; sopranino recorder and bass drum contrasted with recorders, viol, glockenspiels, xylophones, timpani, cymbals, and bass drum.

HOW CAN THE ORFF INSTRUMENTARIUM FACILITATE LEARNING OF OTHER INSTRUMENTS?

The rhythmic training of Orff-Schulwerk provides a student with the foundation for solving any rhythmic problem which might be encountered. Pulse, pattern, accent, meter, changing meter, and phrases of equal or varying lengths are all part of the technical background. One develops rhythmic precision and group sensitivity by playing in the ensemble, and learns cooperation from this participation. An important aspect of this ensemble work is control of dynamic levels. Though difficult for a beginner on any instrument, this control is emphasized from the outset.

The melodic training incorporates some of the factors presented in the rhythmic training: phrases as units for imitation or creative extension, varying dynamic levels, and appreciation of the group as an entity.

Improvisation, and expansion of these elements into form, can take place using the vocabulary the student has acquired. All xylophones, metallophones and glockenspiels are available in diatonic form with extra F# and B♭ bars, and also in chromatic form. Each bar is labeled with a letter name, and all bars are removable so

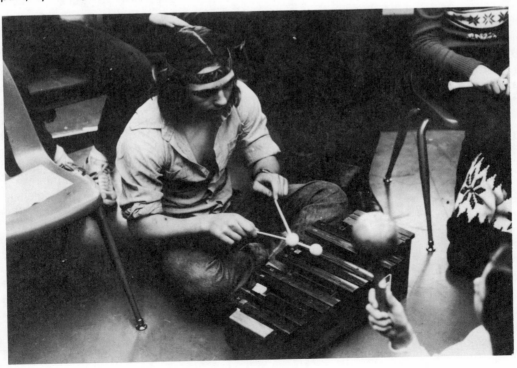

About Improvisation

Isabel Carley

that the teacher may set up limitations within which improvisation can take place. The bars can be visual maps of many kinds of melodic frameworks, including pentatonic, hexatonic, heptatonic, major and minor scales, modes, and tone rows.

Some added advantages: traditional staff notation can be made visible on the barred instruments so that a student can see how the staff works; pitch related to length of the bar is easily understood, regardless of its placement on the sound box; the instruments can show melodic direction, step, and skip; they help to develop a sense of correct pitch for singing, especially when they provide a drone accompaniment. Articulation, legato and staccato effects are experienced with mallet techniques, damping bars or allowing them to vibrate, and special effects created by use of mallets other than the ordinarily designated ones.

All of these elements can be transferred to the study of a band or orchestra instrument.

The child with an Orff-Schulwerk background has had experience in rhythmic and melodic imitation, improvisation, timbre, ostinato and changing accompaniments, and form. Every teacher in the instrumental program should be informed about the wealth of musical knowledge and experience such a student brings to the study of a band or orchestral instrument. While a child is in the initial stages of this instrument instruction, he/she needs the vital musical support which he gets from his continuing to make music in a sophisticated Orff ensemble. When proficiency is reached, on a band or orchestral instrument, the enjoyment of playing an Orff instrument need not be denied; the challenge and fascination of a chamber ensemble remain.

Therefore the Orff instruments can form the basis for further study and also complement that study. More importantly, they can stand alone as valid instruments with which all can make music.

Improvisation is the heart of the Orff approach: improvisation in speech, in movement, in melody, in instrumental play, and not least, in the art of teaching. Carl Orff himself notes this emphasis on improvisation as a unique characteristic of his way of teaching music, an essential part of the process of learning and making music. This emphasis on improvisation, on individual invention, on finding new ways of solving specific problems, is completely in tune with the latest findings and recommendations of our most distinguished and influential phychologists. Abraham Maslow *states, ''We must teach [students] to be creative persons, at least in the sense of being able to confront novelty, to improvise....We need a new kind of human being... who feels strong and courageous and trusting enough to trust himself in the present situation, to handle the problem well in an improvising way, without previous preparation, if need be.'' In an age of rapid change like ours, children need to learn flexibility, independence of thought, faith in their own ideas, and the courage to try, fail, adjust and change until satisfactory solutions are found. There is no surer way than through regular lessons in improvisation.

One of the problems music teachers confront is the product orientation of our culture and traditional music education with its emphasis on performance instead of curriculum. Music has too often been reduced to the level of entertainment, not taken seriously as an essential part of education even by those who teach it. Music teachers who espouse the Orff approach recognize the importance of immediacy, of discovery, of total involvement, of complete concentration on the present synthesis and application, of invention and development. We have Carl Orff to thank for developing simple techniques for teaching improvisation in the classroom day after day through which students are led to a lifelong understanding and enjoyment of music, in whatever direction they choose to go after they leave us.

A basic feeling for pulse, developed through movement and rhythmic play with speech, body rhythms, and nonpitched percussion instruments, and a recognition of pattern, developed through echo play and listening games, underlie the first lessons in improvisation. Improvisation begins with imitation, whatever the age of the students, since aural memory must be developed before a child can distingish between identical and different patterns and phrases. It depends too on familiarity with good models, such as Orff and Keetman have provided, and at least a basic vocabulary of appropriate techniques learned from this first repertoire. In the beginning improvisation may mean only adding a word or a line to make a new verse for a favorite song, or finding a word to match a familiar rhythm pattern. It may mean finding a new body rhythm ostinato to accompany

* Abraham Maslow, The Farther Reaches of Human Nature, Viking, 1971, 88, 97, 98

322

a favorite rhyme, and leading the class with one's own chosen way of saying the rhyme, at a tempo and dynamic level that reinforce one's own interpretation. It may mean using rhythms abstracted from word patterns in new combinations and transferring them to rhythm instruments to make longer forms. It may mean finding one's own way of moving to match a poem, song or rhythm pattern played by teacher or classmate. The possibilities are literally endless, even at this initial stage, and as new skills are developed, still more possibilities are added. In improvisation real choices must be made continually, and taste is gradually developed as more and more satisfying matches are made between materials to be used and their realizations. The same material will never come out the same in two different classes, or in the hands of two different individuals or groups, or even with the same person on two different occasions. There is always room for innovation and experimentation, so that repetition provides the opportunity for change, for improvement. The work of construction, of playing with the elements of music, is never finished.

This kind of immediacy, of freedom to explore and fail and try again until something real and relevant is discovered and worked out, depends on the atmosphere in the classroom. Where there is tension and impatience, confidence evaporates. Success in improvisation lessons and exercises comes from careful planning and patient encouragement. First steps are bound to be halting, but unless these first steps are accepted and encouraged, the whole world of improvisation may be closed to the child for the rest of his life. The climate of the classroom is the teacher's responsibility. Sometimes the establishment of a comfortable climate for growth is made more difficult for a particular class because of tension in the home room from which they come. Sometimes a class comes into music from the playground with such intense animosity brewing between two children that the whole class is upset. It is not an easy task to establish and maintain the emotional atmosphere that nourishes creative work, but it is essential. Improvisation can be one of the surest avenues to emotional stability in the classroom by affording students constructive emotional outlets, challenges custom-tailored to their own abilities, and group recognition.

A hazard of our own making is our desire for conspicuous progress in our classes. In the beginning, progress in improvisation is often discouragingly slow. It takes children brought up on background music or music as entertainment a long time to hear and think music, particularly if there has been no music-making at home. We grow impatient and substitute our own ideas for theirs, allowing them only the task of putting together the ideas we have worked out by ourselves. This is a pretense at improvisation, a travesty of the real thing.

Every music class, every demonstration, every workshop session, should include some opportunity for improvisation, no matter how short. It is essential that each class find something of its very own to use and share and develop in its own way, no matter how simple it may be. Unless time is regularly given to improvisation, the class will conclude that it is not important, that music really means only music in print. How we spend our music time makes our priorities clear. It is then of the utmost importance for the teacher to be at ease with the

323

concept of improvisation and skilled enough to improvise spontaneously in as many different ways as possible, using this skill freely in class, and continuing to work on whatever areas are weak. We need also to cultivate flexibility, to be ready to abandon careful plans when new ideas from the class are suggested, even though we're eager to hear our own ideas and find them more satisfying. Sometimes the new idea doesn't work out, but it is important for the children to discover this themselves. They need to learn what will not work as well as what will. Indeed, one of the main lessons we can learn from improvisation is to make use of our mistakes without interrupting or starting over. The more we improvise, the fewer mistakes there will be. This kind of experimentation takes time and careful guidance from the teacher, both in the choice of assignments and in the kind of evaluation made when the job is done. Each assignment must be clear, within definite limits if it is to be fulfilled successfully. Time must be allowed to complete the job without interruption or criticism, and when it is finished, peer criticism may mean far more than even the most sensitive and considerate criticism from the teacher, although our questions can direct the children's attention to both the strengths and weaknesses of their improvisation.

No one can improvise until he is ready, and different students with the same preparation and training are ready at very different times. It is largely a psychological problem, dependent on feeling at ease enough to concentrate on the immediate task without distraction. It is, therefore, extremely important to let them volunteer for solo assignments when they feel ready, and to allow them to "pass" until they do. First lessons in improvisation, then, must be designed to build confidence and to ensure success. Responses by the whole class or by a group are asked when any new stage is reached, even when the result may be too thick for individual responses to be heard. The process from group to solo improvisation is gradual and lessons need to allow for both. The most confident and inventive students have their off days and they need the discipline of group work, too. We teachers need to beware of falling into the habit of giving the same students demanding assignments time after time when there are others in the class ready for the new challenge, increasingly frustrated at being denied the opportunity of trying their wings.

There are essentially four kinds of improvisation which concern us here. The first is free exploration, which can best be allowed for in speech play, movement lessons, and spontaneous instrumental play, where instruments can be left out for children to use in their free time. Children enjoy using vocal sounds of all kinds, making up nonsense words, playing with range and timbre, both in speech and chant. Melodic improvisation can be introduced through chanting greetings, instructions, rhymes and stories, and encouraging the children to reply in kind. The more the teacher sings, the

more the class will sing. Very often vocal and movement play go spontaneously together as they do on the playground. Children love to explore movement, and there are many ways of stimulating such exploration in the classroom, particularly through mirror play, exercises with individual body parts, and simple movements like walking, running, galloping, skipping and hopping.

The second kind of improvisation involves immediate participation in a given task, a task for which the class is ready and which they can accomplish then and there as soon as the assignment is clear. It need not be remembered or repeated. This stage is reached as soon as the class has learned some basic vocabulary by echoing the teacher, whatever the medium. Possibilities are soon extended with Question-Answer techniques. For instance, a class might be asked to improvise Question-Answer phrases in sets of four all around the class using notes of the G pentatonic scale with E as the tonal center, over a supporting bass xylophone pattern, like this:

Soon the assignment can be made more challenging by asking the first person in each set to repeat his question making an A B A C form like this:

A particularly successful tune may then be used as a Rondo Theme, with improvised episodes by volunteers using a great variety of possibilities, perhaps a four-phrase Body-Rhythm section over a group ostinato, a hand drum solo or duet, a xylophone conversation over a guitar bordun, and recorder Q-A form with BX accompaniment. Introductions and interludes, accompaniment for the theme and contrasting patterns to support the intervening episodes, may be added. Movement may be worked out for the theme, and improvised movement for solo or small group during the episodes, whatever the length of the final rondo.

At this point we begin to move over into the third kind of improvisation, where different groups have different assignments to work out by themselves and bring back to class. Now they must remember what they've done, and be able to reproduce it in public, even after the interruption of hearing another group doing something entirely different. Such assignments take time and much personal attention and encouragement from the teacher. If they are to prove successful, they must be carefully tailored to each group. Texts and dramatic situations give them something to hold onto, and a framework for a longer structure. Even very different sections can be happily joined together in a carnival or a circus. Folk and fairy tales provide endless possiblities for group work. In Red Riding Hood, for instance, one group could be assigned an overture; another, the scene with the mother and child, preparing for the journey; another, Red Riding Hood's walk through the forest and her encounter with the wolf; another, the scene at grandmother's cottage; another, the postlude.

The fourth kind of improvisation involves the whole class in much longer forms, and includes a great variety of techniques which have been learned through experience in the other three. In the beginning, specific assignments to small groups and individuals may be necessary once the underlying "carpet of sound" has been built up. But as time goes on, more leeway may be allowed for spontaneous solo improvisation and group response. Above the entire instrumentarium, vocal and choral improvisation and recorders are most effective. Melodies may be echoed by the group or followed immediately, if the leader uses hand signs. Soloists may subside into ostinati when their inspiration runs dry, alert to respond to the next solo flight. Contrasting sections develop (some vocal, some instrumental) containing contrasting dynamics and mood, with sensitive and unobtrusive leadership and a group of students that is comfortable with each other. The possibilities and delights are endless once the group arrives at a stage of musical sensitivity where it is possible at all.

Whether we are working with speech, body rhythms, instruments, singing, recorders, or movement, the same basic teaching techniques apply. Lessons in improvisation often begin with imitation, with echo play. The teacher is the leader at first, and the whole class responds until some basic techniques and rhythmic "building blocks" have been established. Then a vhild may volunteer to lead the class, to take the teacher's role for a given number of phrases. It is here that real invention first comes into play as the child chooses patterns for the whole class to echo. The next stage is for the teacher to ask for individual volunteers to echo phrases. Then once more a volunteer assumes the teacher's role, and plays phrases for volunteer soloists to echo. Soon the teacher can give individual patterns tailored for each student in turn around the class, leaving out, if necessary, those who are still too insecure to take their turns. Finally, everyone in the class is ready to participate in either role. It is in such lessons that the teacher discovers exactly where each class is, musically speaking and where each individual student is in his or her own musical development. The teacher's role becomes increasingly demanding as the class progresses, since he must be prepared either to repeat his last phrase, if necessary, for the whole class to echo, or to go on to the next student without breaking the rhythm, with a phrase designed just for him.

The same gradual procedure is followed at each successive stage. In Question-Answer work, for instance, the whole class is immediately involved in answering the teacher's question all together, to build confidence; later in asking a prearranged question for volunteer soloists to answer or in playing a pre-arranged answer to improvised questions until the whole class can take part, playing either question or answer all around the class.

Rhythmic ostinati and accompanying patterns on bar instruments may be developed similarly, first by imitating the teacher, then by echoing a volunteer, and finally by taking turns inventing patterns for the whole class to copy. Once the ideas of ostinato, of phrase, of related phrases, have been established, the invention of longer forms becomes possible. In a time-art like music all we

can do, after all, is either to repeat or to do something different. Repetition and contrast are the two formal principles on which all musical forms are built. Play with form, then, can start at the very beginning, as soon as the class has two musical ideas to play with. How many different forms can they find using only two ideas? How can they arrange and re-arrange them to make new combinations? With two phrases given what is the form they hear? What else could they do? What folk song do they know that uses the same form they just invented? Who can make a tune to match the rhythm of phrase A? Phrase B? Which instrument will they choose? What words can be found to match the tune? What patterns can be used to accompany it? What movement can be added to clarify the form and match the mood? One thing leads to another as far as time and imagination permit.

Sometimes, particularly in the early stages, improvisation is stimulated by a text. The rhythm of the words, of the rhyme, may be abstracted from the text, transferred to percussion instruments, or extended and developed with movement. Here the form and character are determined by the words themselves. In the beginning texts may be chosen for the clarity of their rhythm and form from the wealth of playground rhymes that children learn from each other. As time goes on the choice of text becomes ever more important. Anything we teach in depth, as we do in improvisation, will be remembered the rest of the child's life. We need to take time to search for rhymes, stories and poems that are worth this kind of concentrated attention, that are worth a child's remembering instead of settling lazily for the first thing that comes to mind, or using our own poor substitute for poetry invented for the occasion, limping along lamely with false rhymes and unmatched feet.

Similar sensitivity to tone color, dynamics, tempo and ensemble can be gradually improved through lessons in improvisation in which is sought the best possible match of words to instruments, instruments to movement, dynamics to speech or instruments, timbre to melody. Through skillful questions a teacher may lead students to more meticulous use of whatever resources they are ready to handle. Discrimination develops as choices are made and discussed. Gradually the children learn to resist the temptation to use more than can be heard, more than the particular assignment requires. Improvisation, with all the choices it requires, is the best school for taste.

Whether or not the children we teach go on to more sophisticated levels of improvisation and composition, the self-confidence they learn in our classes will remain with them. It is through improvisation that they are most likely to discover their own creative powers for the first time and, having found them to go on to further achievement in whatever field beckons them. Certainly the time spent in improvisation will make better musicians of them as they learn to follow the musical dictation of their own minds, to listen and adjust to the ideas of their classmates and to find the best possible solutions to the problems set for them. Consistent training in improvisation year after year will do much to bring about an education through music that is the goal of the Orff approach.

Performing: Pro and Con

Tossi Aaron

All of us who teach music with Orff-Schulwerk have had a request, at some time, for a demonstration or performance with our children. Such requests present questions, not only of what and how to present our work, but of the value of the performance itself.

Let us ask ourselves first, will it be good for the children? What can be learned or gained from such an experience? What will the audience, though it be composed largely of friends and relatives, perceive and understand of Orff-Schulwerk? Last but not least, is "performance" part of this teaching approach?

As it is in the daily schoolroom, what transpires between the teacher and the children is of primary concern only to them. While many schools have set aside one or two visiting days for parents, teachers are not expected to prepare a demonstration of arithmetic or spelling. Why then should a special program of carefully rehearsed music be expected?

Teaching and working with young children is rewarding and exciting. Their innocent, open way of seeing the world can refresh our tired perceptions, and their curiosity and imagination can help us grow as teachers. While we help them learn about music, we encourage their explorations and discoveries about themselves and their world. However, the rate of development varies so widely from child to child that it is easy to lose sight of the psychological and physiological development that parallels the individual's musical understanding. Certainly, one of the problems of teaching many classes a day is trying to remain aware of these differences.

What can we really expect of a six-year-old? With the excitement of being able to read, to move the body in a coordinated way, and to communicate ideas and feelings, the child's horizons are expanding continually. The skill level in the music class may be quite low by some standards, but perhaps those standards are too high. Do we know when a child is working to full capacity, with intense focus and concentration? Is he feeling pushed by competition, or tense and unhappy with demands that seem beyond his capacity at the moment? Naturally, as teachers, we want to upgrade and increase a student's level of comprehension and skill without superimposing our own expectations, which are born of adult experience and knowledge of what lies ahead. However, we must set individual and group standards within the parameters of their abilities and their experience, rather than our own or those of a printed chart.

For example, true learning progresses through the integration of new ideas and material already assimilated, through experimentation and the making of a form that combines the two in a personal way. Once this exciting discovery is made, the child likes to repeat it many times, fixing it in his ear, mind and hands. (An infant will say new words endlessly!) This repetition is not boring to the child. It is his instinctive practicing, and he must do it to learn. Often it is the teacher who is bored after the sixth repeat. The children understand this repetition and will clearly reflect their pleasure at its result, the innate satisfaction of competence gained. With careful observation, the teacher can tell when that point has been achieved and not press far beyond it.

Although their experience may be limited, we must trust children to know when it is "right", when it "sounds good" or "looks good". Certainly this means trusting ourselves as teachers, trusting that we have helped them become more perceptive, that we have provided good models and sharpened their musical taste, and that we agree with their point of satisfaction and skill.

It is at that stage of any piece or activity that the children are ready to "perform" it, and only at that precise moment in their development. They should then be consulted as to whether they want to present it to anyone else, to share it.

Orff-Schulwerk is first and foremost concerned with and deliberately designed for the process of making music. We can easily lose sight of the goals; to present examples and provide a framework for the children's own work; for their improvisations in a rondo, their movement patterns in a dance, their singing line above an ostinato, their phrase that completes a cadence. When they can do this freely in front of others it reinforces what they have learned and helps them feel valuable to themselves and to the group.

Ideally, such a demonstration should take place in the familiar surroundings of the music room, sharing what they are learning with perhaps only one other class. Should parents be invited, it is most relevant to have only those whose children are in the class. It should be made quite clear at the outset to both children and adults that missteps and fumbles are part of the learning process. Although they like to please others as well as themselves, children understand "mistakes" and therefore will not be crushed by this experience, but will simply pick themselves up and do it again.

Too often, in the demand or desire to put on a good show, it is the teacher and not the students who chooses the program pieces and selects the "best" students to present them. We tend to hide the less capable child behind a tambourine, and we drill endlessly on the material until everyone, ourselves included, is tired of it and glad when the show is over. At the extreme end of this spectrum is the staged production with hundreds of eyes watching, a glare of stage or television lights, and the roar of applause, all of which tend to be outside the children's ability to cope. The emotional expense for all must be considered in striving toward a polished performance.

We all want to be seen at our best, and even the simplest shared class will need some preparation. But it will be up to the skilled teacher to find a mode somewhere between the two extremes, one that makes him/her and the children comfortable. Naturally, a musical presentation that goes well reflects to the credit of the teacher, but we must be sure that the qualities reflected are the valuable ones of sensitivity to the children and faithfulness to the principles of Orff-Schulwerk.

Listening: A Participatory Approach

Jane Frazee

"It has been repeatedly said that the listener likes the music in which he finds himself, in which he recognizes his own emotions and tastes."[1] Many music teachers have, however, persisted in the view that the emotions and tastes of their students could be heightened by encounters with the great masters. Student responses were often predictably indifferent; how could they accept music which had little relation to their life experience?

It is axiomatic that musical communication takes place when the composer's messages and the listener's understanding coincide. Teachers who are interested in introducing young listeners (whose understanding is necessarily limited) to art music (which contains a multiplicity of messages) need to concern themselves with effective means of facilitating communication between composer and listener.

Young students, as a rule, enjoy active participation in learning situations. Partly because of its passive nature, the "listening lesson" often fails to sustain the interest of students, despite the style or quality of the example selected. The constraints of the "listening lesson" can be avoided by regarding listening as only one

of the demonstrable skills of a musical person. Performing and creating also contribute to musical development, and they offer a multitude of possibilities for active participation when integrated with listening and analyzing tasks. The student's interest in all varieties of music can be heightened by his own confrontations with *musical* problems.

Roger Sessions, in his book Questions About Music, offers some helpful suggestions for the development of musical understanding. The listener, according to Sessions, must possess a willing ear, must attend to the sounds, should find a point of contact, then discover more contacts in the piece and related pieces.[2] In classroom terms this means that the teacher first establishes a climate in which many pairs of willing, perhaps eager, ears are encouraged to attend to sounds. Because students need a reason for listening, one that truly matters to them, the teacher might pose a question related to a problem which the class has encountered in a piece performed or composed earlier. Whether this point of contact is a rhythmic fragment, a melodic motive, or any of the other components of musical sound, it should be specific. The extension of this contact point to others in the piece and/or related pieces is a primary characteristic of musical perception.

[1]Chavez, Carlos, MUSICAL THOUGHT. Cambridge, MA, Harvard University Press, 1961, p. 111.

[2]Sessions, Roger, QUESTIONS ABOUT MUSIC. New York, W.W.Norton & Co, Inc. 1970, pp. 13-23.

The following lesson is offered as an example of a participatory approach to listening. It has been designed to introduce Theme and Variations form by encouraging student involvement in performing, listening, analyzing, and creating experiments.

① — Students *sing* Original Theme:

— Students *play* original theme on soprano recorder and/or alto glockenspiel. Add bass xylophone

② — Students *listen* to Bartok "Variations for Piano" to discover the number of variations in the composition

— Students *analyze* the Bartok "Variations" to discover variation devices used in the composition:

Variation 1: Melody transposed to bass register
Variation 2: Texture becomes thicker
Variation 3: Meter changes from triple to duple

Variations

Bela Bartok

③ — Students *play* three variations of original theme to experience the application of Bartok's techniques

Variation 1:

Variation: 2

Variation 3:

④ — Students *create:*
a new theme using F pentatonic tones, with the tonal center on F. A possible bordun accompaniment:

F PENTATONIC

BORDUN

Develop three variations of the new theme based on the Bartok example.

— Students *listen:*
to Symphony No. 31 by Haydn, Movement 4, to discover the number of variations in the composition

— Students *analyze:*
Which familiar variation devices were used in this example? (Texture changes, melody in bass)
What new devices were used? (Elaboration of melody, changes of instruments)

— Students *create:*
two variations for their new theme based on discoveries from the example by Haydn.

The above model can serve any music concept objective which the teacher wishes to pursue. Through integration with other musical skills (creation, performance, and analysis), listening becomes an active, rather than a passive undertaking. As a result of their own creative endeavors, students can develop a growing understanding of musical expression and a deepening insight into its revelations.

Orff-Schulwerk and World Musics — Some Considerations

Mary Stringham-Shamrock

One of the basic principles of Orff-Schulwerk is that the musical material to be used with children at the beginning level to awaken their musical responses should be drawn from the authentic folk heritage of the children's native culture. When the characteristic melodic, rhythmic, and formal patterns have become familiar and comfortable, and when these elements have been internalized sufficiently for the children to express them extemporaneously in new combinations, the process called improvisation, more complex material from the native folk heritage is to be added, material more sophisticated in both textual and musical structure and content but still identifiable with the culture. Concurrently, musical material from other traditions can be added to the repertoire. In most cases this has implied examples from other basically European traditions.

With the growing emphasis on world consciousness, increasing attention is being given to the incorporation of musics of non-western cultures into the body of music used for educational purposes ("non-western" denotes musics with identifiable features which differ from our basically European musical tradition). This trend has not passed unnoticed in Orff-Schulwerk as well as in more traditional classroom approaches. Arrangements are available for folk songs of various cultures with Orff-instrument accompaniment, and purely instrumental compositions have been written which incorporate rhythmic and melodic characteristics of the music of a particular culture, thus giving them an "ethnic" flavor. Such pieces and arrangements are frequently attractive and enjoyable, with the new elements expanding the musical vocabulary of both students and teachers.

The musical cultures based on theoretical and sound systems quite different from the European tradition present a multiplicity of problems to the music educator in terms of making them understandable to students. In some cases, the musical structures of a particular tradition prove to be very similar to those frequently used in Schulwerk music-making–pentatonic and modal scales, ostinato, layered texture, mixed meter, and polyrhythms are examples. In many cases the manner in which the music is learned in the native culture is also comparable to what is considered typical in Schulwerk—that is, learning both rhythm and melody by listening and imitating, with no benefit of musical notation. With these factors in mind, some teachers have experimented with using the Orff instruments as substitutes for those of a particular non-western musical culture. The various parts of a piece, ideally a simple but authentic example from the culture itself, are learned and assembled into a performable totality, and in theory at least, a piece from an unfamiliar tradition is being played in a rather authentic style, with the Orff instruments simulating the timbres of the traditional ones. Two styles that have been explored in this way are the Indonesian *Gamelan* tradition and polyrhythmic African drumming.

Before a potentially limitless expansion into other musical traditions is attempted, some basic questions need to be considered; questions concerning the goals of such an expanded musical perspective. Are we trying to add zest and variety to Schulwerk music making, and find in world musics attractive elements which suit this purpose? Or are we actually attempting some in-depth exploration of the unfamiliar music which will lead to a new degree of understanding not only of that music but of the culture itself?

The incorporation of elements of other cultures into our daily lives, for the purpose of adding variety and interest, is increasingly common in this age of world accessibility. We eat Indian curry on Japanese *sukiyaki*, wear a *dashiki* or *kimono* without making any pretense of trying to further our understanding of the cultures in which these items originated. All too often travel is approached in a similar manner. People hastily pass through a series of countries, absorbing the sights, sounds, and smells, and return home with a degree of experiential enrichment, to be sure, but no essential deepening of understanding of the cultures they have visited.

To return to the consideration of music, the question is whether or not this type of enrichment of vocabulary, stimulating though it may be, is sufficient to be supportable as musical "education." Proponents of world consciousness and understanding would not be convinced. Music is not an isolated phenomenon in any culture; rather, it reflects the social, philosophical, and religious structures of the society. The attitude of the society toward music and the making of music is frequently quite different from our own, which in itself reveals significant differences about the societies involved.

It might be suggested that the simplest way to avoid the entire issue would be not to use music of unfamiliar cultures as teaching material. In the United States our present situation renders this impossible. The classroom of children that in reality has a homogeneous heritage is extremely rare at present. More frequently the children come from many backgrounds of race, religion, nationality, and life style. What is perhaps unfortunate and more difficult to deal with is that many of them identify with no tradition at all, so that music presented as being part of a native folk heritage will in reality be as strange and unknown as any other. The musical "culture" of these children consists of what they hear around them every day, and that includes elements from many different cultures and sub-cultures. Most of it falls into what is considered the European tradition, although elements from non-western cultures have increasingly found their way into the various musical idioms being explored by composers and performers of today.

One advantage of today's multi-faceted listening environment may well be that the children growing up in it do not find the sounds of other musical traditions as unusual or unpalatable as we may expect. They may be ready to listen to and deal with the authentic sound in a way no previous generation could have done.

Given the necessity of including musics of various traditions and cultures in music education for children, teachers could be tempted to view the resources of the Orff-Schulwerk approach as a panacea; the directions one could take are indeed limitless. We must not be afraid, however, to examine the limitations of these resources for introducing and exploring musics of other cultures. Playing world musics with Orff instruments, whether it be incorporating certain elements into a basically Schulwerk-style composition or attempting to play a completely new style, is a compromise at best; the responsibility of determining the degree of acceptable compromise lies with the teacher. Especially in non-western musics, the pitches and timbres may be so far removed from what can be simulated on Orff instruments that even attempting the style becomes a travesty of good taste. Certain techniques may appear deceptively accessible. Improvisation is a case in point: what may seem to be a completely spontaneous spinning out of musical ideas in an unfamiliar musical tradition is often in actuality an artistic rearrangement or resynthesis on the part of the performer of intricate rhythmic and/or melodic patterns which have been memorized and perfected. The point is that in certain situations Schulwerk resources will not be appropriate, and the teacher must exercise the good judgement not to use them.

So where should the music teacher begin in trying to cope with this situation? Is it not the duty of the classroom teacher to introduce children to the non-musical facets of world cultures? And how can the music teacher be expected to be conversant with the great diversity of musical styles and traditions of the world? As a beginning, focus on a limited area is recommended. It seems reasonable that a thorough study of one new culture and its music will be a far more meaningful introduction, both for the teacher and the students, than a superficial overview of a multitude of unfamiliar styles. Opportunities for teachers to learn about world musics, both western and non-western, have just begun to develop; appropriate college courses, summer workshops and in-service training are essential if any real change in the direction of education toward world understanding, here specifically toward world musical understanding, is to be effected. More cooperation between teachers and administration than is customary or convenient may be required to structure comprehensive, in-depth learning experiences. In any case, responsibility must be assumed for the cultural implications of the musical materials being presented if such presentation is to be considered "education."

The resources of Orff-Schulwerk include a wealth of tools, both of sound and of pedagogy, which can be utilized to expand the understanding and enjoyment of world musics. The extraordinary potential for actually involving the children in appropriate movement and music making cannot be ignored. The challenge presented here to the Schulwerk teacher is to utilize these resources with good taste and with insight and sensitivity toward the musics and cultures under consideration.

About Dance Notation

Miriam Samuelson

For centuries dancers have attempted to find a way to communicate the steps and floor patterns they have developed for their movements. This was important for social dance forms and for dance as a theatrical art. These include the dance steps of the chorus in the dramas of ancient Greece, the historical *pavans, galliards* and *branles*; English court and contra dances; classical and modern choreographies for the stage; international folk dances and the elemental forms we present in this volume.

Thoinot Arbeau, in *Orchesography* (1589), solved the problem using for the most part a verbal description of the dances which included proper posture, gestures of courtesy and specific steps shown in direct reference to the dance melodies. He also included instructions for the musicians. John Playford, in *The English Dancing Master* (1651), used the symbols of ❯ and ⊙ for differentiating men and women dancers respectively and introduced a particular vocabulary to describe room formations... "Longways for as many as will..." and specific steps... "Up a double, forward and back..." and... "Set and turn single...". During the past 300 years a great variety of symbols and systems has been worked out. More recently, Rudolf von Laban developed an extensive system of graphics for the notation of dance movements, steps, floor patterns, postures, etc. This has become one of the most accepted notations for the professional dancer and choreographer. Classical ballet choreographers prefer Benesh Notation, and there are still other contemporary systems of dance notation, most of which need a long time to study. In our elementary choreographies we have also had to find a way to communicate clearly and as simply as possible ideas for movement forms and specific dances. Children should be encouraged to discover ways to write down their dances just as they find ways to notate their melodies and improvisations. Notating music or a dance clarifies and helps one to memorize movement sequences or songs by bringing ideas to a concrete form. Because dance is more visual than aural, filming or videotaping is the most precise way of recording movement for choreographers, dancers, teachers and children alike.

The following dance notation legend has been developed for our purposes here. One can always find other possibilities.

Dance Notation Legend

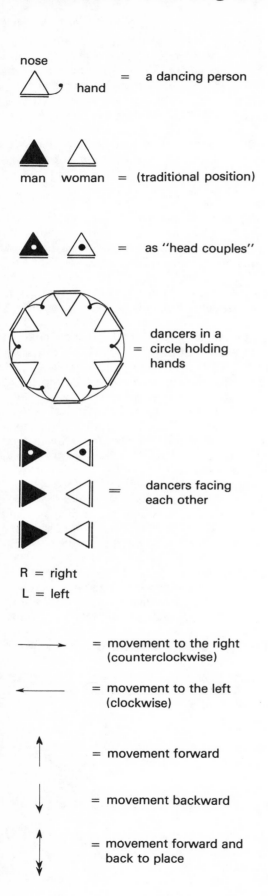

nose

△ , hand = a dancing person

▲ △
man woman = (traditional position)

▲ △ = as "head couples"

= dancers in a circle holding hands

▶ ◀

▶ ◀ = dancers facing each other

▶ ◀

R = right

L = left

⟶ = movement to the right (counterclockwise)

⟵ = movement to the left (clockwise)

↑ = movement forward

↓ = movement backward

↕ = movement forward and back to place

↺ = a turn in place (counterclockwise)

♩ = right foot

♩ = left foot

♩ = both feet come together

♩ = hop (on right foot)

(♩) = touch foot without weight

♩ ♩ = one foot crosses in front of or behind the other

= rhythm of the steps

Although most of the dances in this volume call for partners of men and women, it is not necessary to make a differentiation in this way. It is possible to clarify the movements of each partner by having one dancer wear, for example, a marker of a special color.

334

We thank the publishers concerned for their kind
permission to use their materials.

For advice, translation and arrangment of materials
we thank

Victor Dal Pozzal
Jane Frazee
Elsbeth Hörner
Verena Maschat
Miriam Samuelson
Carolee Stewart
Ruth Vickery

ORFF-SCHULWERK AMERICAN EDITION

About the Index...

Listed are:

— Contributors: If no name appears, the contribution is
   public domain.

— Activities: Movement, speech, singing, instrumental
   playing, etc.

— Accompaniments: Indicating the kind of setting for a
   given piece. It was not always possible to make a definite decision about an "either/or" situation... mix-
   tures occur frequently. It can happen that an AX
   plays an ostinato while the BX plays the basic tones
   of a cadential harmony in a non-ostinato way. In such
   cases dots may appear in three columns.

— Tonal Material: Determined according to the melody,
   not the accompaniment. With modal melodies only
   the general character can be defined. The modes
   have not been listed separately. In the column under
   "2-6 tones" the notes in the melody are listed only as
   a matter of statistics. In some cases a dot has been
   added in another column which determines the tonal
   center more clearly, even when the scale is in-
   complete.

This index is intended to help the teacher find specific
material quickly. For example, "I am looking for a song in
minor with cadential harmonies." A check of the corresponding columns in the index will present a number of
choices. This new form of index was necessary to make
the volumes accessible as resource material in a flexible
way which will meet the needs of children and teachers.

INDEX

Page Number	Title Number	Title	Contributor	Sample Lesson	Song	Song with Foreign Text	Canon	2-Part Song	3/4-Part Song	Speech Piece	Developmental Text	Rhythmic Exercise	Less Familiar Meter	Free Rhythm	Instrumental Piece	Improvisational Development	Compositional Exercise	Movement Response	Movement Form	Dramatic Response	Notation Skills	Accompaniment: Sound Gestures	Accompaniment: Vocal Ostinato	Accompaniment: Instrumental Ostinato	Accompaniment: Instrumental Non-Ostinato	Accompaniment: Cadential Harmonies	2/3/4/5/6 – Tone	Major	Mi
2	1	Old Ark	Jane Frazee				●			●														●			●	●	
4	2	Ungaresca	Maureen Kennedy			●																		●	●		●	●	
7	3	Patsching Exercises	Miriam Samuelson	●								●																	
8	4	Savila Se Bela Loza	Miriam Samuelson												●				●					●		●		●	
10	5	Smile in Your Pocket	Nancy Ferguson						●															●			●	●	
12	6	Sourwood Mountain	Arvida Steen		●													●						●			●	●	
15	7	An Experience with a piece from "Musik Für Kinder"	Martha Pline	●											●									●			●	●	
18	8	Six Instrumental Pieces	Orff-Schulwerk Musik Für Kinder I/126 I/123 I/121 I/120 I/114 I/128												●									●			●	●	
24	9	Movement with Props	Marcia Lunz	●												●		●											
25	10	Entendez-vous Le Carillon?	Martha Pline			●	●																	●			●	●	
25	11	How Many Miles to Bethlehem?	Isabel Carley				●																	●			●	●	
27	12	The Little Black Bull	Isabel Carley		●																			●			●	●	
29	13	The Machine	Erik Nielsen	●										●		●		●			●								
30	14	Ghost Dance Song	Isabel Carley		●																			●			●		●
31	15	Penobscot Song of Greeting	Isabel Carley			●																		●			●		
32	16	Maori Indian Battle Chant	Nancy Ferguson			●										●		●									●		●
33	17	The Ball Game	Lynn W. Johnson	●								●						●		●									
34	18	Rhythmic Exercise: Canon	Miriam Samuelson	●			●					●																	
35	19	Drum Canon	Isabel Carley				●			●		●			●														
37	20	Liebe ist ein Ring	Maureen Kennedy				●																	●			●	●	
42	21	Canon	Jane Frazee				●																	●			●		●
43	22	Týnom, Tånom	Miriam Samuelson			●	●																	●			●		●
44	23	Four Shaker Songs	Martha Pline		●														●					●			●	●	
49	24	Charlie	Isabel Carley		●					●	●											●		●			●		●
52	25	Sail Away Ladies	Patsy Smith		●																			●			●	●	
54	26	Soldier, Soldier, Will You Marry Me?	Patsy Smith					●												●				●			●	●	
62	27	Improvisation with Text	Jane Frazee	●						●						●								●					
62	28	Two Poems	Miriam Samuelson								●																		
63	29	Patsching Exercise	Miriam Samuelson	●								●																	

INDEX

Page	Title Number	Title	Contributor	Sample Lesson	Song	Song with Foreign Text	Canon	2-Part Song	3/4-Part Song	Speech Piece	Developmental Text	Rhythmic Exercise	Less Familiar Meter	Free Rhythm	Instrumental Piece	Improvisational Development	Compositional Exercise	Movement Response	Movement Form	Dramatic Response	Notation Skills	Sound Gestures	Vocal Ostinato	Instrumental Ostinato	Instrumental Non-Ostinato	Cadential Harmonies	2/3/4/5/6 — Tone	Major	Minor	Modal	Extended Tonality
4	30	What's Old Women Made of?	Isabel Carley		•																		•				•	•			
6	31	The Pease Branle	Miriam Samuelson/ Cynthia Campbell												•			•					•							•	
8	32	Weeping Mary	Jane Frazee		•																		•							•	
9	33	An Old Story	Tossi Aaron												•				•				•					•	•		
0	34	Two Canons	Martha Pline				•								•								•			•				•	
2	35	Listening to Haydn	Jane Frazee	•							•									•											
3	36	Jimmy Randal	Maureen Kennedy		•																		•							•	
6	37	Dance	Miriam Samuelson/ Cynthia Campbell												•			•			•		•							•	
8	38	A Nonsense Rondo	Isabel Carley		•														•			•	•					•	•	•	
4	39	Big-Eye Rabbit	Konnie Saliba		•																		•					•	•		
7	40	Follow the Leader	Isabel Carley			•										•	•						•					•		•	
9	41	Wade in the Water	Jane Frazee		•																		•							•	
1	42	Recorder Rondo	Jane Frazee												•	•							•							•	
2	43	The Seasons: A Rondo in Four Parts	Sue Ellen Page		•										•	•		•					•					•	•		
0	44	Ostinato Exercises	Miriam Samuelson	•								•			•					•		•	•								
5	45	Lions	Konnie Saliba		•																		•	•	•	•				•	
0	46	The Good Old Man	Maureen Kennedy		•								•											•	•	•				•	
1	47	Dundai	Miriam Samuelson/ Cynthia Campell												•			•						•	•					•	
5	48	Never a Child as He	Patsy Smith		•		•																•	•		•				•	
8	49	Oh, Jerusalem	Patsy Smith		•																		•	•						•	
1	50	The Mysterious Cat	Donald Slagel		•								•										•					•		•	
5	51	Compositions	Lynn W. Johnson	•													•	•	•		•										
6	52	Instrumental ABA	Donald Slagel												•			•						•	•	•			•	•	
8	53	Oh, Suzanna	Cynthia Campbell																	•											
9	54	Developing Chord Changes (I-V-I)	Miriam Samuelson	•													•							•	•	•		•			
1	55	Fod	Tossi Aaron		•																•			•	•		•				
2	56	Black Eyed Susie	Konnie Saliba		•																		•	•	•		•				
4	57	Cumberland Reel	Cynthia Campbell																	•											
6	58	Working with Poetry	Maureen Kennedy	•	•					•		•		•										•	•		•				•
9	59	Poems Poor Old Jonathon Bing I Don't Know Why the Sky is Blue There Once Was a Witch Good Night Mr. Beetle	Konnie Saliba								•																				

INDEX

Page Number	Title Number	Title	Contributor	Sample Lesson	Song	Song with Foreign Text	Canon	2-Part Song	3/4-Part Song	Speech Piece	Developmental Text	Rhythmic Exercise	Less Familiar Meter	Free Rhythm	Instrumental Piece	Improvisational Development	Compositional Exercise	Movement Response	Movement Form	Dramatic Response	Notation Skills	Sound Gestures	Accompaniment: Vocal Ostinato	Instrumental Ostinato	Instrumental Non-Ostinato	Cadential Harmonies	2/3/4/5/6 — Tone	Major
140	60	Ersatz Liadl	Miriam Samuelson												•			•						•	•	•		•
141	61	Praised be the Lord	Jane Frazee					•								•								•	•		•
143	62	All 'Round the Ring	Jane Frazee	•	•			•	•									•	•					•	•	•	•	•
146	63	El Tren Por Almendral	Isabel Carley				•	•								•								•	•	•		•
149	64	Saeynu	Jane Frazee				•	•																	•			•
151	65	Creole Tune	Judith Thomas	•												•		•							•			•
152	66	Broom Man	Jane Frazee		•											•								•	•			
153	67	Shifting Accents	Arvida Steen	•	•					•			•		•			•				•		•			•	
155	68	Gustaf's Skoal	Cynthia Campbell															•										
157	69	Cinquain	Maureen Kennedy	•						•																		
158	70	Old Walt	Donald Slagel		•																			•	•		•	•
161	71	Riding Round the Cattle	Isabel Carley		•																	•		•			•	
165	72	Developing Chord Changes (I-IV-V-I)	Editorial Example	•												•	•			•				•	•			•
167	73	Dashing Away With the Smoothing Iron	Orff-Schulwerk III/84 Music for Children		•																			•	•			
169	74	Lullaby	Ruth Pollock-Hamm		•																			•	•			
170	75	Banuwah	Jane Frazee				•																					
172	76	Sun Magic	Jane Frazee		•																			•	•			•
174	77	Janie Mama	Martha Pline				•															•						•
178	78	A Writing Lesson Expanded	Judith Thomas	•													•	•										
179	79	May Song	Isabel Carley				•				•																	
180	80	It is the Tears of the Earth	Jane Frazee				•			•	•					•		•					•					
181	81	A Hand was Fill'd	Jane Frazee							•				•											•			
182	82	Baby Song of the Four Winds	Jane Frazee							•											•				•			
183	83	A Little Nonsense / The Crocodile / Similar Cases / Kilkenney Cats / What! / The Peacock / The Time Has Come	Isabel Carley								•																	
184	84	Refugee in America	Donald Slagel		•																			•				
186	85	Shabat Shalom	Jane Frazee			•																		•	•	•		
189	86	Developing Chord Changes (i-iv-v/V-i)	Editorial Example	•												•	•			•				•	•			
191	87	Go Down, Moses	Donald Slagel		•																			•	•			
198	88	Have a Music Olympics	Judith Thomas													•	•	•										

338

INDEX

Page Number	Title Number	Title	Contributor	Sample Lesson	Song	Song with Foreign Text	Canon	2-Part Song	3/4-Part Song	Speech Piece	Developmental Text	Rhythmic Exercise	Less Familiar Meter	Free Rhythm	Instrumental Piece	Improvisational Development	Compositional Exercise	Movement Response	Movement Form	Dramatic Response	Notation Skills	Sound Gestures	Vocal Ostinato (Accompaniment)	Instrumental Ostinato (Accompaniment)	Instrumental Non-Ostinato (Accompaniment)	Cadential Harmonies (Accompaniment)	2/3/4/5/6 – Tone	Major	Minor	Modal	Extended Tonality
01	89	Boomba	Jane Frazee			●							●											●	●	●		●			
04	90	Changing Meter Dance	Jane Frazee									●	●					●						●	●			●			
07	91	Handing Exercise	Miriam Samuelson	●								●																			
08	92	Water Come-a Me Eye	Jane Frazee		●																			●	●						
11	93	Puppets to Polished Performance	Judith Thomas	●														●	●												
12	94	Rose Tree Contra	Cynthia Campbell															●													
14	95	The Busy Bass	Jane Frazee	●								●					●				●			●				●			
15	96	Lamento	Orff-Schulwerk Musik für Kinder V/42												●									●	●	●			●		
15	97	Carillon	Orff-Schulwerk Musik für Kinder V/47												●									●	●					●	
16	98	Nottamun Town	Isabel Carley		●							●												●	●					●	
17	99	Canon in 5	Miriam Samuelson				●					●			●	●								●						●	
18	100	Metamorphosis	Donald Slagel	●								●												●						●	
26	101	Ev'ry Night When the Sun Goes In	Becky Pinnell				●																	●	●				●		
36	102	Thus Saith the Lord	Donald Slagel					●				●					●							●						●	
45	103	The City	Jane Frazee							●														●							
46	104	From "Song of Exposition"	Jane Frazee							●	●													●							
47	105	Two Rhymes to Change Time	Jane Frazee							●			●											●							
48	106	Go 'Way from My Window	Jane Frazee		●																			●	●	●					
50	107	A Flea and a Fly	Isabel Carley							●		●										●	●	●							
58	108	Developing Chord Changes (I-vi-ii-V)	Editorial Example	●													●				●			●	●			●			
59	109	Old Blue	Donald Slagel				●																	●	●			●			
64	110	Scherzo	Miriam Samuelson												●									●						●	
66	111	Life is Fine	Donald Sagel		●																			●						●	
68	112	The Fairy Tale of Teeny-flea and Weeny-Louse	Orff-Schulwerk Musik für Kinder V/117								●									●				●							
71	113	Entrad, Pastores, Entrad	Isabel Carley			●	●																	●	●			●			
77	114	Two Villancicos from Puerto Rico a) Feliçes Pascuas Señores	Isabel Carley			●	●						●											●	●				●		
79	114	b) Vamos Pastorcitos	Isabel Carley			●							●										●							●	
80	115	More Compositions	Lynn W. Johnson	●												●	●	●		●											
81	116	Turtle Dove	Martha Pline		●																			●						●	
84	117	Allegro in Lydian Mode	Miriam Samuelson												●	●								●						●	
85	118	The Ins and Outs of Texture	Judith Thomas	●												●	●														

339

INDEX

Page Number	Title Number	Title	Contributor	Sample Lesson	Song	Song with Foreign Text	Canon	2-Part Song	3/4-Part Song	Speech Piece	Developmental Text	Rhythmic Exercise	Less Familiar Meter	Free Rhythm	Instrumental Piece	Improvisational Development	Compositional Exercise	Movement Response	Movement Form	Dramatic Response	Notation Skills	Sound Gestures	Vocal Ostinato	Instrumental Ostinato	Instrumental Non-Ostinato	Cadential Harmonies	2/3/4/5/6 – Tone	Major	Minor
286	119	Dream Dust	Donald Slagel		•																			•					
288	120	Rhythmic Exercise	Miriam Samuelson	•								•	•				•												
289	121	St. Ives	Donald Slagel		•								•				•							•			•		•
291	122	Mixolydian Dance	Tossi Aaron												•			•	•					•					
292	123	Sellenger's Round	Cynthia Campbell														•												
295	124	Lollipop	Ruth Pollock-Hamm	•							•						•												
296	125	Loneliness	Jane Frazee							•					•										•				
297	126	Making a "Tone Row" Piece	Martha Pline	•												•	•					•							
298	127	Schönberg Study	Erik Nielsen											•								•				•			
299	128	Poem	Miriam Samuelson								•																		
299	129	The Tickle Rhyme	Miriam Samuelson								•																		
299	130	Our Washing Machine	Ruth Pollock-Hamm	•							•					•		•		•			•						
300	131	I Am a Bird	Erik Nielsen		•										•										•		•	
302	132	Kulu #2	Erik Nielsen	•											•										•		•	
304	133	Todas Las Tardes	Erik Nielsen		•										•										•			
305	134	The Seafarer	Erik Nielsen							•				•	•										•			
314	135	The Little Mute Boy	Erik Nielsen		•						•				•										•			
318	136	Poems In the Night (Konnie Saliba) Weather Words (Miriam Samuelson) The Point, the Line, the Surface and Sphere (Miriam Samuelson)									•																	

ALPHABETICAL INDEX

Title No.

llegro in Lydian Mode 117	It Is the Tears of the Earth 80
ll 'Round the Ring 62	Janie Mama 77
pril Rain Song 58/3	Jimmy Randal 36
aby Song of the Four Winds 82	Kulu #2 132
all Game, The 17	Lamento 96
anuwah 75	Liebe ist ein Ring 20
ig Eyed Rabbit 39	Life is Fine 111
lack Eyed Susie 56	Lions 45
oomba 89	Listening to Haydn 35
room Man 66	Little Black Bull, The 12
usy Bass, The 95	Little Mute Boy 135
anon 21	Little Nonsense, A 83
anon in 5 99	Lollipop 124
arillon 97	Loneliness 125
harlie 24	Lullaby 74
hanging Meter Dance 90	Machine, The 13
inquain 69	Making a Tone Row Piece 126
ity, The 103	Maori Indian Battle Chant 16
ome Dance and Sing 23/1	May Song 79
ome Life, Shaker Life 23/3	Metamorphosis 100
reole Tune 65	Mixolydian Dance 122
umberland Reel 57	More Compositions 115
ance 37	Movement with Props 9
ashing Away with the Smoothing Iron 73	Mysterious Cat, The 50
eveloping Chord Changes (I-V-I) 54	Never a Child as He 48
eveloping Chord Changes (I-IV-V-I) 72	Night Wind 51B
eveloping Chord Changes in Minor (I-IV-V-I) 86	Nonsense Rondo, A 38
eveloping Chord Changes (I-VI-II-I) 108	Nottamun Town 98
ream Dust 119	Oh, Jerusalem 49
rum Canon 19	Oh, Suzanna 53
undai 47	Old Ark 1
l Tren por Almendral 63	Old Blue 109
ntendez-vous le Carillon? 10	Old Story, An 33
ntrad, Pastores, Entrad 113	Old Walt 70
rsatz Laidl 60	Ostinato Exercises 44
v'ry Night When the Sun Goes in 101	Our Washing Machine 130
xperience with a Piece . . ., An 7	Patching Exercises 29
airy Tale of Teeny-Flea and Weeny-Louse, The 112	Patching Exercises 3
lea and a Fly, A 107	Pease Branle, The 31
od 55	Penobscot Song of Greeting 15
ollow the Leader 40	Pickety Fence, The 58/2
our Shaker Songs 23	Poem 128
host Dance Song 14	Poem in Your Pocket 5
o Down, Moses 87	Poems 59
ood Old Man, The 46	Poems 136
o 'Way from My Window 106	Praised Be the Lord 61
ustaf's Skoal 68	Puppets to Polished Performance 93
Handing " Exercise 91	Recorder Rondo 42
and Was Fill'd, A 81	Refugee in America 84
ave a Music Olympics 88	Rhythmic Exercise 120
op Up and Jump Up 23/4	Rhythmic Exercise: Canon 18
ow Many Miles to Bethlehem? 11	Riding Round the Cattle 71
am a Bird 131	Rose Tree, The 94
mprovisation with Text 27	Saeynu 64
ns and Outs of Textures, The 118	Sail Away Ladies 25
nstrumental A-B-A 52	Sellenger's Round 123

Savila Se Bela Loza 4
Scherzo 110
Schönberg Study 127
Seafarer, The 134
Seasons, The: A Rondo in 4 Parts 43
Shabat Shalom 85
Shifting Accents 67
Simple Gifts 23/2
Six Instrumental Pieces 8
Soldier, Soldier, Will You Marry Me? 26
"Song of Exposition", From 104
St. Ives 121
Sun Magic 76
Sourwood Mountain 6
Thus Saith the Lord 102
Tickle Rhyme, The 129

Todas Las Tardes 13
Tren por Almendral, El 6
   (Train to Sante Fe, The)
Turtledove 11
Two Canons 3
Two Poems 2
Two Rhymes to Change Time 10
Two Villancicos from Puerto Rico 11
Tynom, Tanom 2
Ungaresca . . . .
Wade in the Water 4
Water Come-a Me Eye 9
Weeping Mary 3
What's Old Women Made Of? 3
Working with Poetry 5
Writing Lesson Expanded, A 7